WITHDRA
ISLINGTON

G000089436

THE BRIDE'S MIRROR

THE BRIDE'S MIRROR

MIRĀT UL-'ARŪS

A Tale of Life in Delhi a Hundred Years Ago

Maulvi Nazir Ahmad

Translated from the Urdu by
G.E. Ward

With an Afterword by
Frances W. Pritchett

ISLINGTON LIBRARY

LIBRARY

CLASS No.

CAT'D

DATE

WITHDRAWN FROM ISLINGTON LIBRARIES

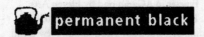

permanent black

Published by

PERMANENT BLACK
D-28 Oxford Apartments, 11, I.P. Extension,
New Delhi 110092

Distributed by

ORIENT LONGMAN LTD.
Bangalore Bhopal Bhubaneshwar Chandigarh
Chennai Ernakulam Guwahati Hyderabad Jaipur
Kolkata Lucknow Mumbai New Delhi Patna

This edition copyright © PERMANENT BLACK 2001

All rights reserved

ISBN 81-7824-021-1

First published 1903

Typeset in AGaramond by Eleven Arts
Printed by Pauls Press, Delhi 110020
Binding by Saku Binders, Khanpur, New Delhi

CONTENTS

TRANSLATOR'S NOTE

T his translation is merely supplementary to an edition of the
original text in the Roman character, which was published in
1899, and intended as a text-book for students in Hindustani.
It makes no claim to literary merit; but since so little is known in England
about the social and domestic life of our Indian fellow-subjects, an
authentic picture of one phase of it by a distinguished Muhammadan
gentleman may perhaps be not devoid of interest to the British public
in general.

G.E. Ward
1903

PREFACE

✦

IN THE NAME OF GOD THE COMPASSIONATE THE MERCIFUL

Thanksgiving to the bountiful Lord by the widest range of my eloquence could never be rendered. To essay the requital of His lovingkindness and a thousand times ten thousand benefits—

'Little mouth, big words!'

Eulogy of our master the Prophet by all the strength of my feeble will could never be expressed. To pretend to any recompense for his tendernesses and fervencies of heart—

'*This* mite of a creature, a yard of tongue'

After praise (of the Most High) and commemoration (of His apostle), be it known that:

Although it is not the custom in this land to teach reading and writing to the secluded sex, still, in the big cities there are a few good families of which the women, as a rule, do keep up the practice of reading among themselves the translation of the glorious Qur-án and the vernacular treatises on the precepts and doctrines of religion. Of such a family, belonging to Delhi, I thank God that I am a member.

In accordance with the family custom, my daughters also were taught by the elder ladies of the house to read such small vernacular tracts as 'The Holy Qur-án and its Teaching', 'A Letter on the Last Day', 'The Way of Salvation', etc. It was a house in which reading and writing formed a constant topic of conversation at all times. I noticed that even my little daughters, taking their cue from us men, had quite a longing of their own for the acquisition of knowledge. At the same time, however, I became convinced that purely religious subjects of study are not suited to the capacities of children, and that the literature to which my children's attention was restricted had the effect of depressing their spirits, of checking their natural instincts, and of blunting their intelligence.

I then tried to find some kind of book—well stored, of course, with moral instruction, and which should improve their ideas and correct their habits in respect of those affairs which a woman encounters in her daily life, and in which, by reason of their romantic notions, or through ignorance or perversity, so many women are overtaken by disaster and sorrow, and yet which should be in a form sufficiently attractive to prevent their being discouraged or dismayed by its perusal. But though I searched and searched for such a book through a whole library of volumes, not a trace of one could I find.

It was then that I formed the design of the present tale. The story of Akbari was put into shape three years ago, when I was at Jhansi. My daughters made it their daily task to read it, and they began pestering me every day to complete the book, until, a year and a half later, the story of Asghari also was written.[1] By degrees the book came to be talked of in the mohulla. A few women came in to listen when it was being read, and all who listened were charmed with it. The manuscript was borrowed for perusal in some great houses. Applications were made for permission to take copies of it. In the meanwhile my eldest daughter's marriage took place. I included the manuscript in her dower, as a jewel of great price, and it achieved no less a reputation in her new home.

Having satisfied myself that the book was really very useful for women, and that they took the greatest interest in reading it or hearing it read, I then submitted it, through the Director of Public Instruction, North-West Provinces, to the Government of the Provinces. The generous appreciation of the Government has raised my own estimation, as well as the value of the book, more than I dare to express. My wishes have been realized, and my labour rewarded to my heart's content.

[1] Apparently the first instalment of the book concluded with what is Chapter VII, in the translation.

Besides the time originally spent in the composition of this work, I have devoted many hours to its revision, in my desire to attain simplicity of diction, as well as purity of sentiment, and to prevent the intrusion into any passage of what is far-fetched or unnatural. Since the book is of a character entirely new, it is not unlikely that some blemishes may still have been overlooked. These I beg my readers to excuse, on the ground that this is absolutely the first original work of *its kind* in the language.

The servant of God,
Nazir Ahmad

(*May God dispose him to make provision for the morrow!*)

INTRODUCTION

IN THE NAME OF GOD THE COMPASSIONATE THE MERCIFUL

No one more thoroughly deserves to be called 'stupid' than a human being who does not sometimes ponder over the affairs of the world we live in. And although there are fit subjects for meditation in this world of a thousand different kinds, the most fundamental and important of all is human life itself.

Just consider—from the day that a man is born, until he dies— what a number of different things happen to him in the course of his life, and what wonderful changes he himself is constantly undergoing. The best time of all in a man's life is that of childhood. At that age he has no kind of anxiety. His father and mother cherish him with the utmost tenderness and affection, and, as far as their means go, provide him with every comfort.

Parents take a pleasure in their children being well fed and well clothed, and for the sake of their children's comfort are content to undergo all kinds of annoyance and trouble. Men who are fathers earn money—some by the roughest manual labour, some take up a profession, some go into trade, some into service; in short, by whatever means are available, they find the money required for their children's ease. Women who are mothers very often work hard themselves to make money if the father's earnings are not sufficient for the household expenses. This one takes in needlework, another knits lace, another makes men's caps—nay, there are some mothers, stricken by calamity, who are maintaining their children by grinding at the mill, or spinning at the wheel, or doing the work of a general drudge in a house.

The affection which parents have for their children is not pretended, or put on for show. On the contrary, it is genuine love which springs from the heart, and God (be He exalted!), who is all-wise, has planted this fondness for their offspring in fathers and mothers in order that the offspring should obtain proper nourishment. At the commencement of their life the little things are extremely helpless—unable to speak, or to understand, to move or to get about. If their parents did not lovingly tend them, little children would die of hunger. Whence should they get bread? Whither would they go for clothes? And how would they grow up to be big?

Is it the case only with human beings? Even among animals the love of their young is very strong. How carefully does a hen bring up her chickens! All day long she keeps sitting and hiding them under her wings; and if she finds a single grain of corn anywhere, *she* does not eat it; she calls the chickens, and lays it in front of them with her beak; and if a hawk or a cat wants to attack them, without a thought of her own safety, she is ready to fight and be killed for them. It is clear, then, that God has given this special affection to parents for no other reason than this—that the supply of such tiny little creatures' needs should never be checked; that they should get food when they are hungry, water when they are thirsty, warm clothing to shield them from the cold, and everything requisite for their comfort at the right time.

Experience teaches us that this special affection only lasts so long as the young are dependent upon it for their needs. When a hen's chickens grow big, she leaves off hiding them under her wings, and as soon as they run about, and are able to fill their own crops for themselves, the hen does not give them any assistance. Indeed, when they get very big, she begins to peck at them in such a fashion you might suppose she was not their mother.

The same is the case with human parents. So long as the child is very small the mother nurses it, and carries it about with her wherever she goes. She gives up her whole night's rest, while she is patting the baby to sleep. But when the child is old enough to begin eating 'khichri', the mother leaves off nursing it altogether, and that milk which she has gone on giving to it so fondly for many years she now withholds from it persistently and sternly. She applies bitter-tasting things (to keep the child away), and if the child is pertinacious she slaps and scolds it. After a time the children come to a stage in which her taking them up into her lap even is an annoyance to her.

Have you never seen your little brothers and sisters getting slapped because they would not leave their mother's lap? Mother gets angry, and says: 'What a troublesome child it is! Not out of my lap for a moment!' Do not suppose from this that her love no longer remains. The fact is, that there are different *kinds* of affection during different stages of existence. The state of children does not always remain the same. Today they are drinking milk; tomorrow they have begun to eat food; by-and-by they learn to walk. As a child goes on getting bigger, so the tone of the parents' love for it goes on changing. How many a beating do boys and girls get over their reading and writing! Although little children in their folly may not think so, even the pain which comes to you from your father's or mother's hands is really conducive to your own advantage.

You will have many days to live in the world after you are separated from your parents; no one yet has ever preserved his father and mother alive for the whole of his own term of life. Happy indeed may those boys and girls be called, who during their parents' lifetime acquired the common sense and good habits which have enabled them to pass their whole lives in joy and peace; and very evil is the fate of those children who never valued their parents' existence, and made no use of the advantages which their parents' efforts secured to them, but wasted the precious time of unruffled leisure in playing and idling, and have since spent their lives in trouble and misfortune. They have lived in torment, and they made their parents also live in torment on their account.

It is not a question only of dying. During the lifetime of the parents, their children slip away from their control as soon as they are married. And by the time that children come to be of middle age their parents are old people, and themselves become dependent upon their children; so that sons and daughters, after they have reached that age, so far from being assisted by their parents, have to support and relieve them.

Boys and girls ought certainly to consider how their life will be passed after they are separated from their parents. In this world the heaviest burdens fall upon the males of a family. The food, the clothes, and all the things which are required for daily consumption, are in this world procured by money. The chink of *rupees* sets men's teeth on edge.

It is a happy thing for women that, as a rule, they are preserved from the toil of earning a livelihood or making money. Look at all the hard work of different kinds which is performed by men. One carries huge loads on his head; another brings in firewood. The goldsmith, the blacksmith, the tinker, the brazier, the gold and silver wire-maker, -beater, -flattener, -drawer, -gilder, the jeweller, the embroiderer, the silver-thread-twister, the metal-worker, the enameller, the tin-washer, the plain-worker, the burnisher, the mirror-maker, the gold-lace-maker, the lacware-man, the shoeing-smith, the seal-engraver, the shoe-embroiderer, the hone-cutter, the sand-sifter, the caster, the carpenter, the turner, the cocoanut-worker, the comb-maker, the bamboo-splitter, the paper-maker, the weaver, the tent-maker, the dyer, the calico-printer, the tailor, the turban-maker, the braid-maker, the tube-maker, the cobbler, the die-cutter, the stone-mason, the lapidary, the builder, the leather-worker, the potter, the sweetmeat-seller, the oilman, the pawn-seller, the colour-maker, the perfumer—it does not matter what trade a man is of; in *all* of them there is the same amount of irksome toil and labour, and all this labour is put up with and undergone by men for the sake of earning money.

But for all this you must not suppose that women have no share at all in the business of the world beyond eating and sleeping. On the contrary, it is the women who do the entire work of housekeeping. The man brings his earnings home, and lays them down before the women, and they, with their woman's wit, make the money go so far, by economy and good management, that not only the comfort, but the credit and respectability, of the family defy reproach. So that, if you look into the matter carefully, the world is like a cart which cannot move without two wheels—man on one side, and woman on the other. Men cannot spare the time from their breadwinning occupations to spend on the little details of household management.

You boys must learn those things which will be useful to you when you are men; and you girls should acquire those gifts which will be a source of pleasure and profit to you when you are women. No doubt God has created women, in comparison with men, of a somewhat more delicate physique; but He has given to women hands, feet, ears, eyes, intelligence, thought, memory, just the same as to men.

These are the things which boys make use of, and with their help become great scholars, reciters, doctors, artists, mechanics—supreme in every craft, adepts in every science. Girls who waste their time in playing with dolls or listening to stories are left in a state of ignorance. And yet there are women—those who have understood the value of time, and have spent it in useful pursuits—who have become famous and celebrated in the world in the same way as men. Such women were Núr Jehán begam, and Zebunnisa begam; and in these days the nawáb Sikandar begam,[1] or the English Princess, Queen Victoria. They are women who have administered the affairs of nations—of the whole world, not of a little home and family.

Some ignorant women reason after this fashion. They say: 'However much we read, shall we become *maulavis* like men? Well, then, what is the use of our bothering ourselves?' But even if a woman has learnt more than she requires, there is not the least doubt she will reap a proportionate advantage. I do not deny that too much learning is unnecessary for a woman, but how many women are there who acquire even so much as is absolutely necessary? It is of the greatest importance to them, at the very least, to be able to read and write the vernacular. If they have not *this* amount of learning, they are certain to be put to inconvenience. Either they are compelled to disclose their own family matters to strangers, or they incur all the annoyances that may arise from keeping them secret. The subjects which occupy a woman's thoughts are usually of a delicate and private nature, but it is often necessary for her to communicate them to a mother or a sister; and suppose that by any chance her mother or sister are not near her at the time? In such a case she must either lay her modesty upon the shelf, or she must endure all the evils that result from her silence.

[1]Núr Jehán, the celebrated wife of the Emperor Jahángir, died A.D. 1645. Zebunnisa, daughter of the Emperor Aurangzeb, died unmarried A.D. 1702. Sikandar begam, ruler of Bhopál, died A.D. 1868.

Writing is certainly a little difficult in comparison with reading, but any person who will make a practice of copying out four lines a day from a book, and of writing that amount over again from memory—getting the exercises corrected—in a few months, at the outside, will have learnt to write. There is no call for elegant penmanship;[2] mere writing is an art which is of the greatest use in emergencies. If there are mistakes, or if the letters are ill-formed or incorrect, don't give up your practice in despair. Whatever it be, no work is done well at the beginning. You might give some great scholar one of these skull-caps to cut out and sew together, but if such a thing had never happened to him before, it is certain he would make a mess of it.

This moving about on your legs, which is now so easy to you that you run here and there at your pleasure—very likely you don't remember with what difficulty it was learnt; but it is well within the recollection of your parents and elders that first of all you could not even sit without support. When they took you out of anyone's lap, and put you on the ground, someone kept hold of you, or they placed a cushion to prop you up. After that, by tumbling about, you learnt to crawl on your knees, and then to stand up, but holding on to the bed-stead; then, when your legs became stronger, you gradually learnt to walk; but every day one heard of your falling, and hundreds of times you hurt yourselves. And now here you are, by the grace of God, running about in the most astonishing way.

One of these days writing will come to you just as easily. But suppose that you never are able to write quite so well as boys; without a doubt you will at least be able to write sufficiently well to meet your own requirements, and you will no longer be put to the inconvenience of having to get up and draw lines on the wall, or make little heaps of gravel or pebbles, in order to check the clothes sent to wash, or the reckonings of the woman who grinds your corn. To keep all the accounts of the house—what there is to receive, and what there is to pay—entirely by rote is a very difficult matter, and it is a way with some husbands to ask for an account every now and then of the different

---

[2]Among the Musalmans calligraphy is one of the fine arts. Single specimens of a few lines written by eminent calligraphists fetch prices analogous to those given in England for etchings by celebrated artists.

sums they have paid towards the household expenses. If the wife cannot remember the items pat, the husband gets suspicious and says to himself: 'Where has all that money gone?' Then the one gets annoyed with the other, all about nothing, and a quarrel is the result. If women would only learn so much writing as would enable them to be accurate in their own accounts, what a good thing it would be!

Besides reading and writing, two other arts are very necessary for girls to learn—namely, needlework and cooking. None of us know what contingencies may meet our paths in the future. The greatest nobles, the richest men are reduced to poverty and beggary at a moment's notice. If they happen to be masters of any kind of skill, it stands them in good service during their time of need. It is a matter of history that the kings of former ages, notwithstanding all their wealth and magnificence, invariably trained themselves to learn some handicraft, which might prove useful to them in the time of misfortune. Remember that no position in this world is secure. If at the present moment you are in the enjoyment of perfect ease and security, give thanks to God that of His great goodness He has blessed your home with such prosperity and affluence. But this does not mean that you should underrate the value of your present good fortune, or that you should take it for granted, in looking to the future, that the same amount of comfort will be your lot for ever.

In the time of prosperity it is most important to keep your conduct and daily habits up to the mark. Although God may have given you servants to wait upon you, it is your business to see that *you* don't get spoilt. If (which God forbid!) your present opulence should not last, *that* would cause you much annoyance. Not to get up even to drink a glass of water—to give trouble to the servants, or to your younger brothers and sisters, for every little thing you want, while you are lolling at ease like some old State pensioner, is conduct unsuited to your age, and is evidence of a spoilt disposition. You ought to do all your own things for yourselves; indeed, if you are active and on the alert, you can do many things for the house, and if you are willing to take a little trouble, you can give a great deal of help and assistance to your mother.

Think over this well, and don't leave any of your business so that your mother will have to do it with her own hands, or be distracted by calling others to do it, and so giving trouble to them.

Yes, my dear little girl! When you go to bed at night, spread out your bedding for yourself with your own hands, and in the morning get up betimes and fold it up, and put it carefully in its proper place. Keep your own bundle of clothes under your own charge, and whenever you wish to change any of your clothes, and put on something else, first mend whatever is torn or has come unstitched in it with your own hands. Be careful about the dirty clothes. Until the washerwoman comes for them, hang them up separately on pegs. If, when you change your clothes, you do not pick up the dirty ones, perhaps the rats will gnaw them to bits; or they may get more dirty by lying about, and the washerwoman will not be able to clean them properly; or perhaps, on account of damp in the ground,[3] or the moisture of perspiration, white ants will get at them. And always see your clothes yourself before giving them to the washerwoman; and when she brings them back from the wash, look them over before you take them; perhaps she may have brought less than the full number, or she may have torn them somewhere, or there may be some stains not taken out. If you look after your clothes in this way they will always be washed beautifully clean, and none of them will ever be lost.

The ornaments which you wear are things that cost a great deal. In the evening, before going to bed, and in the morning, when you get up,[4] you should notice whether they are all there or not. It often happens that heedless girls let some of their ornaments fall while they are playing about, and then perhaps days afterwards they find out that an earring has dropped off, or a ring is missing from its place. After the house has been through ever so many cleanings, how can anyone

---

[3]The floors as well as the walls of many rooms even in the best houses are made of beaten earth, and are constantly kept clean, cool, and fragrant by the process of 'leeping—'i.e., washing them over with a solution of a particularly fine clay mixed with fresh cowdung.

[4]It is by no means an uncommon occurrence, among the poorer classes at all events, for women to be robbed of their ornaments while they are asleep. In the hot nights they sleep on the flat roofs of the houses or in their courtyards under the sky.

tell where a tiny little thing like that has gone to, or whereabouts in the ground it has got trampled under foot? Then the careless girls cry and bewail the loss of their ornaments, and throw the whole house into confusion in searching for them. Moreover, when the parents see that a girl does not take any trouble to look after her own jewellery, and is always losing it, they, too, begin to be somewhat chary of their benevolence.

You ought always to be on the watch for any little jobs in the work of the house which you can make it your business to do. When your little brothers and sisters cry, or are troublesome, you can surely undertake to keep them quiet, so that your mother may not be worried by them. The washing of their faces, looking after their meals, putting on their clothes—all these things, if you have the will, you have the power to do. But if you want to have your own way, and fight with them, you lower yourselves in their estimation, and cause your mother extra trouble. Is she to look after the work of the house, or to be always adjudicating your disputes?

You ought not to watch the meals being cooked in the house with no other object than to find out how soon they will be done, and when you will get them. If the dog, or the cat, or any other animal that may be a family pet—if *they* lie waiting till dinner is ready, in the hope of filling their stomachs, it is no great matter. But *you* ought to be taking note of everything that is done—how the seasoning is prepared and fried, how much salt they put into the different dishes. If you watch the preparation of each meal carefully, I am sure that before very long you will learn how to cook yourselves, and then you will have acquired an art which of all arts in the world is most indispensable.

Besides the ordinary articles of diet, you ought to learn how to prepare some dishes of ceremony. In entertaining chance guests it is always desirable to have a few extra delicacies. Kabábs, pulá-os, sweetened rice, zarda, matanjan, chutnies, preserves, firní, are all of them tasty dishes, and you ought to learn the receipt for every one of them. And there are some dishes which are not of a sumptuous character, and yet to cook them nicely is a thing to be proud of, such as fish and karelas.

Sewing is not so very hard to learn, but cutting out requires some ingenuity. Put your heart into it, and learn how it is done. You cannot get on without it, and especially the cutting out of women's clothes. I have seen many a woman, who ought to have known better, carrying her draperies about to other women, in the hope that they will cut them out for her; and for such a trifling matter as this she has to do a lot of coaxing and wheedling. Of men's clothes, the jacket is certainly rather difficult. You should try the plan of cutting out your brothers' jackets. After you have done three or four you will soon get into the way of it.

Although girls are too shy to speak of such things, they know well enough in their hearts that the days of their girlhood will not last much longer. Some time or other they will be married. And after being married, they will have to live an entirely new kind of life, such as you see your mother, and *her* mother living, as well as your aunt and all the ladies of the family. The time of maidenhood is short, and, indeed, the greater part of it is spent in your infancy. A new life, like a hill which you have to climb, is coming nearer and nearer, and it is full of all kinds of perplexities and trials.

Now, you must bear in mind that you are not girls of any abnormal creation, so that, after marriage, you should meet with exceptional good luck. What happens to all the married girls in the world will happen to you. Well, then, just consider what sort of life it is which women lead. What degree of honour is theirs after marriage? What *kind* of respect do men pay to them, and in what sort of ways do they try to please them? Do not look at the cases of special individuals. Sometimes it happens that there is an excess of affection, and the wife gains the mastery over the husband; and where there is an extraordinary want of affection the wife's authority is completely thrown aside. These are exceptions to the rule. But look at the general custom, and the common practice of the whole country. According to that standard, I for my part see *no* value set upon women. 'Wanting in intellect', serves as their title. 'Woman's obstinacy', 'Woman's ways', are phrases always on men's lips. There is a passage in the Qur-án condemning the wiles of women: *'Verily, as to your deceit, it is appalling.'* Men take it for granted that the female sex is not trustworthy, as in the line:

'Horse, Lady, or Sword—fit to be trusted, who has seen!'

One poet has even found an excuse for maligning them in the etymology of the word which means woman:

If all of her actions were kind and discreet,
Her name would be 'Beat not'—it would not 'be Beat'.[5]

All these things are written in books. Look into the conduct of family life. Beyond the mere drudgery of housekeeping, is any help in matters of outside importance ever sought for from women, or are they consulted or referred to for advice in any really important business? Why, even in houses where the greatest respect and consideration is shown to the women, when any *questions* are asked of them, this is the style: 'Eh, my dear! what vegetables will be wanted for cooking to-day?' 'Do you wish me to order the girl's new shoes with a figured pattern or a border?' 'Will you have Manikchundi betel or jahází?' 'Do you prefer Bengal tobacco, or Amánat Khán's?' 'Is the quilt to have a purple edging or of antimony colour?' I ask any woman to tell me whether, beyond this, men have ever taken her advice in important deliberations, or have left any important business to her discretion.

If this be the case, women of India, does not a life led under such conditions ever strike you as being unsatisfactory? Do you never lament over your insignificance and want of responsibility? Do not your souls long for a higher kind of esteem in the eyes of men? It is you yourselves who have allowed your authority to slip out of your own hands. It is your fault that you are so fallen in the estimation of the world. If the capacity for business were in you, how long would it be before men recognised it? If you were competent to give advice, where is the man who would not respect it? Here lies the difficulty. You women consider it an adequate endowment for the duties of life if you are just able to cook chapatties and dal, and to mend torn or worn clothes. Well, your value in the world is on a par with your endowments. In the condition in which you now are—not only folly, not only deceit and insincerity— if all the charges in the world were hurled against you, it is not without

[5]The Persian word for 'woman' is 'zan', which word is *also* the imperative form of the verb 'zadan', to beat. The prohibitive form is 'mazan', 'beat not'.

reason; and if every kind of evil be imputed to you, it is not without grounds. Oh women! you are the joy of men's hearts, you are the source of all the happiness in their lives, you are the delight of their eyes, you are they who multiply men's pleasures and beguile their pains. If men could get help from you in great matters, if you had the faculty of common sense for managing great matters, why, men would drink the very water in which they had washed your feet, and would make you the enduring crown of their existence. Have they any other consolers better than you, or advisers better than you, or friends better than you?

But if you are to acquire the capacity for dealing with great matters, how is it to be done? You are shut up within the four walls of the house; you can see nobody, you can talk to nobody. Knowledge, whether it be theoretical or practical, is transmitted from one human being to another. Men do acquire both kinds of knowledge by a literary education, but even those who are illiterate mix with people of different conditions numbered by thousands. From every ten men they hear ten new ideas.

For you there is little hope of escape from your seclusion. Public opinion and the customs of the country have made a retired life behind the purdah obligatory and incumbent upon women, and in these days the observance of this institution is more rigid than ever.

Hence, except reading and writing, there is positively no method by which you can develop your intellects. Indeed, if you compare them with men, the need of education for women is even greater: For, since men admittedly live an out-of-door life, they will pick up the experience they want by associating with other people. But you, who sit at home all day long, what will you do? Will you fish out a little packet of common sense from your sewing-bag, or fetch a napkinful of experience out of the grain-closet? Learn to read, and while you are seated behind the purdah you may make a tour of the whole world. Get knowledge, and without going outside the house you may become acquainted with what has happened in all the ages.

If for no other reason, for the sake of educating their children, it behoves women to get all the culture they can. Girls are brought up at home as a matter of course, until they are married, and so are most boys until they are ten years old. The influence of their mother's character and companionship leaves its mark upon them. The whole future life of your children, therefore, is in your power. You may either instill into their hearts from their earliest youth such good desires and noble ambitions that, when they grow up, they will gain the esteem of their fellow-men, and, spending their lives in tranquillity, will never cease to be grateful to you; *or* you may so pervert their natural instincts that the older they grow the more they will become demoralized, and such a commencement of their life they will bemoan until its close.

As soon as boys can speak they have the capacity for instruction. If the mothers are properly qualified, they can begin to educate them from that moment. While boys are waiting to be sent to school many years of their life are practically lost. At a very early age boys have no inclination to go to school, and even if they had, the maternal instincts of their mothers would rebel against the notion of little children, not yet able to control their own physical exigencies, being put under the iron rule of a school-master. But their mothers, if they are so disposed, can teach them a great deal during these years. And even after the boys have begun to attend school they learn their lessons for a long time in a half-hearted way, and days and days go by before any real progress is made in their studies. During the whole of this time they can receive immense assistance from their mothers. To begin with, where is there anything like a mother's sweetness and sympathy? And then the mere fact of their being always together night and day—whenever they see that a boy's attention is roused, in a second they can get him to recognise the shape of some letter, or they can impress on his memory some arithmetical fact, or they can make him understand the difference between east and west. Mothers can teach in the course of conversation what a school-master cannot teach in years of tuition; and there is this inestimable advantage in a mother's teaching—that, while the boy gets every incentive to greater diligence, there is not the least chance of his being frightened.

So far I have dwelt only on the moral training of the children; but the arrangements for their physical well-being—even the preservation of their lives—depend also upon the mother's will. If (which God forbid!) there be anything lacking in their capacity for these duties, it is an evil case for the children's very existence. No one would be such a wretch[6] as to speak a word in disparagement of maternal fondness. Yet it is quite possible that this very fondness, if exercised without knowledge, may have the opposite effect of what was intended, and cause harm instead of good. I appeal to your candour whether there are not thousands of mothers who are so ignorant and silly that they attribute every illness of their children to an evil eye, or a malignant shadow, or to some seizure, or the influence of devils, and so, instead of giving them medicine, perform all kinds of magical charms and exorcisms. What is likely to be the result of such ill-suited remedies I leave it to you to imagine.

To sum up. The successful management of a household in every detail depends upon a sound judgment, and the cultivation and correction of the judgment depends upon the acquisition of knowledge. And now I am going to tell you an amusing story, which will show you what kind of troubles are brought about by a bad education.

[6]Lit., 'Who is such a man (bad luck to him!) who would have a word to say!' etc.

CHAPTER

I

❧

There was a silly girl whose marriage had taken place, but from sheer want of common sense she could not manage to spend even a year or two under the roof of her husband's parents. In the fourth or fifth month after the wedding she began pestering her husband to take a separate house for her, because, forsooth, she was 'unable to stand' his mother and sisters.

Her husband said: 'In all of your squabbles with my mother and sisters which I have happened to overhear, it is you who have been in the wrong. Whatever people there are of the commonest sort living in the mohulla,[1] you treat *their* daughters as if they were your sisters. *Chuniya*—the daughter of Bhondu the sutler, and *Zulfan*—the daughter of Bakhshu the tinker, and *Rahmat*—the daughter of Kimmu the water-carrier, and *Sulmati*—the daughter of Maulan the greengrocer,[2] are received by you with open arms at all hours of the day, and you take no account of the fact that these people are not of our family, or connection, nor admitted to our society or friendship. The whole mohulla is talking about it, and saying, "What sort of a bride has come here now? Whenever you see her, only girls of *that* sort are sitting with her." After all there are people living in the mohulla—people, too, like Kázi Imám Ali, Hakím Shifá-uddaula, Munshi Mumtáz Ahmad,

[1] Our nearest equivalent to 'mohulla' (which is spelt in the English fashion) is 'ward'; it means a collection of houses in a city known by one name.

[2] Pronounce Chooniya, Bhoandoo, Zoolfun, Bukhshoo, Ruhmat, Kimmoo, Soolmuttee, and Mowlun.

Maulavi Rúhulláh, Mír Hasan Rizá[3]—whose daughters and daughters-in-law are in the habit of visiting us. You don't vouchsafe a word
to any of *them*. If my honoured mother warned you against associating
with girls of low-bred and vulgar people, what was there improper in
her doing so?'

The silly wife replied: 'Affection and friendship depend upon the
union of hearts. There was a bangle-seller named Básu living next door
to my mother's house, whose daughter Banno was my bosom friend.[4] I
used to play with her when I was little. Yes, Banno and I made a marriage
between our two dolls. Banno, poor thing! was very badly off. I used to
steal quantities of things from my mother and give them to her. I would
never give up my meetings with Banno, however much my mother
forbade them.'

Her husband said: 'A precious idiot you were, then!'

When she heard this, the foolish woman cried out to her husband:
'Look here! by God's oath, I tell you once for all—you must keep a
smooth tongue when you speak to me, Sir. Else, I'll dash my brains
out, so that you shall have my blood on your head.' And upon that she
began crying, and cursing her father and mother. 'Oh God! be it bad
for such parents! What a miserable lot they have thrust me into!
Everyone knows I am helpless, and so they are bent on persecuting me.
Oh God! let me die! Let my bier be carried out!'

And in the height of her passion she kicked over a little pawncasket[5]
which had been left on the bed and upset it. All the catechu and lime
was spilt on the mattress. A coverlet of English woolen-stuff had been
folded back over the foot of the bed; as soon as the lime touched it, all
its colour was taken out. On hearing the clatter of the box falling, her
mother-in-law came running from the saloon on the opposite side.
The son, when he saw his mother coming, took himself off by another

---

[3]Pronounce Hakím as Hukeem, Munshi as Moonshee, Hassan as Hussan. The
'á' with an accent is the long 'a' in 'father'; the 'ú' the long 'u' in 'ruler'; 'í' has the
value of 'ee'.

[4]Pronounce Barsoo and Bunno.

[5]A box (probably of silver) with compartments containing fresh leaves of the
'piper betel' (pawn) and the various ingredients that are put inside the leaf, which
is then wrapped up and chewed.

doorway; but he said to himself as he left: 'Well, I *have* stirred up a hornet's nest for my sins!'

When the mother-in-law came in, what does she see! A whole anna's worth of catechu—which she had only put into its cup the day before, after carefully straining and preparing it—all lying spilt, the mattress sticky with it, the coverlet soaked with lime, her daughter-in-law weeping and sobbing convulsively. Directly she entered she clasped her daughter-in-law to her neck, and wildly uttered many hard words about her son.

The moral support derived from *this* show of sympathy became a pretext for further action, as irresistible as the proverbial 'a jogger to a nodder.' No amount of entreaty or expostulation on the part of her mother-in-law had the slightest effect upon this hypocritical woman. All the females of the neighbourhood, when they heard the noise of crying and slapping,[6] gathered in a crowd at the door. At last matters came to such a pitch that Zulfan, the daughter of Bakhshu the tinman, ran off to the bride's mother's house, and there rehearsed a story of the affair, in which every incident was magnified fourfold. Now the bride's mother also, by the grace of God, was a very hot-tempered woman. The instant she heard the story she got into her doolie and arrived at the spot. There was a battle royal between the two mothers. In the end, the bride's mother took the bride away with her. For several months all ordinary civilities between the two families were entirely suspended.

In order to make my story intelligible, I must tell you the names of all these people. Akbari Khánam was the proper name of this foolish and deceitful woman, and in her husband's home she had received the title of Mizájdár bahu.[7] Although this Akbari was foolish and ill-educated and bad-tempered, her younger sister Asghari[8] was a very intelligent, sensible, and kindly dispositioned girl. At an early age she had read through the translation of the Qur-án and the vernacular text-books

[6]*i.e.*, slapping the breast as a sign of lamentation.

[7]Pronounce Ukburee and Buhoo, with the accent on the first syllable in each case. 'Bahu' means 'bride' or 'daughter-in-law'; 'Mizájdár' may mean in a good sense 'one who has a proper sense of her dignity', and in a bad sense 'one who has a temper.'

[8]Pronounce Usghuree, with accent on the first syllable. The words Akbari and Asghari simply mean 'elder' and 'younger'. Khánam means 'lady'.

of religious doctrine; and in writing, too, she was not at a loss. Every week she used to send a letter containing the family news to her father. She could do every kind of needlework, and knew how to cook quite a variety of tasty dishes. The whole mohulla sang her praises. All the arrangements of her mother's housekeeping were left in her hands. Whenever her father came home on privilege leave, he would consult her in his management of the family affairs. The ready money, the keys of the store-cupboard and boxes—in fact, everything of the kind was left under her control. Both of her parents were exceedingly fond of her, and, indeed, she was beloved by everyone in the mohulla; but Akbari, for no reason at all, was always on bad terms with her younger sister, and at times used even to strike her when she found her alone. And yet Asghari invariably treated her elder sister with respect, and never told tales of her to her mother.

It so happened that both sisters became betrothed into the same family. Muhammad Aqil[9] and Muhammad Kámil[10] were two brothers. Akbari had already been married to the elder brother, Muhammad Aqil, and Asghari's engagement to Muhammad Kámil had been definitely arranged, but the marriage had not yet taken place. In consequence of Akbari's display of bad temper, Asghari's betrothal was very nearly being broken off; but there was an aunt on the mother's side of the two girls, who lived close by Muhammad Aqil's house, and she always exerted a good influence over them. Although Akbari had left her husband after a regular quarrel, her aunt denounced her conduct in very plain terms, and lost no opportunity of admonishing her. And, finally, after several months, she took the opportunity of the Ramazán[11] to bring her niece back, and get her received in her father-in-law's house. For some days, indeed, Muhammad Aqil continued to view his wife with displeasure, but at length the good aunt got both husband and wife to be reconciled to each other. Still, when there is no real harmony in the dispositions of two people, occasions for umbrage are to be found in all kinds of little things.

One day, Muhammad Aqil said to his mother: 'I have invited a

[9]Pronounce Moohummud, with accent on the second syllable, and Arckill.
[10]Pronounce Karmil.
[11]Pronounce Rummuzarn, with accent on the last syllable.

friend to come in. It would be as well if the food at fast-breaking time[12] and supper were served up with a little extra care.'

His mother replied: 'Heaven knows what I suffer in cooking even the bread for our supper. At fast-breaking time, for the last three days, I have been seized with ague, so as not even to know what I am about. God bless the woman next door for cooking that, even as well as she does! You really ought to have made some inquiry in the house before inviting anyone.'

Muhammad Aqil glanced towards his wife with a look of amazement, and said: 'What! is she not even fit to help you in that?'

Don't suppose that his wife had sufficient self-control to keep silent when she heard such a remark as this was. No sooner had the words caught her ear than she called out: 'Ask this old mother of yours whether she got her son married, or purchased a slave-girl for him. What! toil over a kitchen fire in fast time? Not I, Sir.'

Muhammad Aqil thought to himself: 'Now, if I make any kind of reply, there will be the same disgraceful scene as before.'

With a look of blank disappointment he held his peace, and fetched in some things for the fast-breaking from the bázár. So that matter was got over.

---

[12]During the fast a very light meal is taken directly after sunset.

CHAPTER

II

⚜

B ut Muhammad Aqil was now confronted by a new calamity—
namely, the Eed.[1] The poor man had commenced his preparations for Mizájdár bahu's new outfit a whole week before. Every
day he brought home cloths of different kinds, bangles of different colours,
embroidered shoes of this or that pattern; nothing met with Mizájdár's
approval, until at last there was only one day left before the Eed. In
despair he went off and called at the house of Akbari khánam's aunt.

As soon as she heard his voice, she summoned him in to the ladies'
apartments, and greeting him with blessings, affectionately made him
sit down by her. Then she prepared some pawn, and having handed a
leaf to him, she said: 'Tell me, is Akbari all well?'

Muhammad Aqil replied: 'Madam, your sister's daughter is a woman
of a marvellous constitution; she quite takes my breath away. Her
vivacity is something extraordinary, and her conversation is made up
of contradictions.'

His Aunt said: 'My dear son, don't worry yourself about it. She is
quite young now. When she has children, when she feels the burden
of keeping house, her temper will get right of itself. And, after all,
good people do manage to get on with bad people. God has endowed
you, my son, with every kind of advantage. Don't let anything happen

---

[1] *i.e.,* the great feast on the first day after the Ramazán. It is a day of thanksgiving
and reconciliation, and all who can afford to do so wear new clothes. The word
is spelt here according to the English pronunciation of it.

at which people might jeer. After all, it is your own honor which is at stake.'

Muhammad Aqil said: 'Yes, your honor, and simply on that consideration I do try to overlook a great deal. But just think of this: tomorrow is the Eed, and up to this moment she has not tried on her new bangles, nor made up her new costume. Would you come over for a moment and bring her to her senses? I have said all I could, my mother has entreated her, but she won't listen to a word.'

His Aunt said: 'Very well. Your uncle has just gone to the mosque for prayers, but as soon as he returns. I will ask him, and come over.'

Accordingly, the good aunt came to the house, and made the girl put on her new bangles, and did the cutting-out of the clothes. For greater speed, all the women sat down together to sew. The aunt said: 'Daughter, do you put the frills on to the trousers. Your mother-in-law will cut the trimmings, and, meanwhile, I will stitch the edging on to your mantle.'

When Akbari had finished putting on the frills, she said to her Aunt with a consequential air: 'Here, Lady, you have still two sides left, and I have already finished putting the frills on both legs.'

Her Aunt looked at the frills; they were put on upside down. Out of respect for Akbari's mother-in-law she did not say anything out loud, but she managed quietly to give Akbari two or three pinches, which brought tears into her eyes, and she made a gesture as much as to say: 'Good for nothing! Can't you see? You have put the frills on upside down.'

Akbari undid all her sewing, and began putting the frills on again. When she had done, her Aunt looked, and they were all in puckers. This time the Aunt lost her temper, and without letting Akbari's mother-in-law see, she ran the point of her needle into Akbari's hand; and after undoing the frills a second time, she put them on herself. In the end, after many groans and supplications,[2] Madam Mizájdár bahu's new costume was at last sewn together and completed. A good part of the night had gone. Akbari's aunt departed to her own home, and the people of the house, too, wished each other good-night and went to bed.

---

[2] Lit., 'after many a Lord! Lord!'

For joy of the Eed, the children woke up betimes in the morning. One took off the henna wrappings of the night, another shouted out for oilcake and gram flour,[3] another began demanding the Eed presents the instant he arose. Muhammad Aqil, too, as soon as his morning prayers were over, went off to the *hammám*[4] for a bath, and came back, clean and spruce, shortly after day-break. He found all the boys sitting ready, with their new clothes on, to go to the Eedgáh.[5] But Mizájdár bahu, according to her usual custom, was fast asleep. Muhammad Aqil said to his little sister Mahmúda: 'Go, Mahmúda, and wake up your sister-in-law.'

At first Mahmúda hesitated; she was very much afraid of Mizájdár bahu, who, from the day she was married, had never once spoken kindly to her little sister-in-law, or let her come near her, or sit by her side. But in the joy of the Eed, at her brother's request, Mahmúda ran off, and said: 'Sister-in-law! Get up!'

Her sister-in-law did get up, and simultaneously caught Mahmúda a slap full in the face. Mahmúda began to cry. Her brother, hearing her voice, ran in and asked what had happened.

'Sister-in-law struck me,' said Mahmúda, still crying.

Mizájdár called out: 'Oh what a liar! Oh what a good-for-nothing! She fell of herself as she was running, and puts it upon me!'

I need hardly say that Muhammad Aqil was very angry; but thinking it the best plan at the time, he restrained his indignation, and quieted Mahmúda with kisses and caresses. Then he said to his wife: 'Well! get up and bathe, and put your new clothes on. The day is far advanced; I am going to the Eedgáh.'

Mizájdár turned up her nose and frowned, and said: 'I don't bathe so early as this; it is cold. Go to your Eedgáh; have I said anything to the contrary?'

At this cross speech Muhammad Aqil was extremely annoyed; but Mizájdár was by nature so unlucky that she was for ever keeping her husband in a state of vexation with her.

[3]For washing.
[4]Pronounce hummarm. The bath is what is known as 'a Turkish bath'.
[5]A wide enclosure generally built outside a town, at which *all* the Muslims assemble for prayer on the Eed.

Meanwhile, Muhammad Aqil's mother called to him: 'Son, dear, just go and fetch some milk from the bázár. You can easily go to the Eedgáh afterwards.'

Muhammad Aqil said: 'All right, give me the money, and I will bring the milk; but if by the time I come back this girl has not changed her clothes, I will put them all on the kitchen fire.'

So saying, he went off to the bázár for the milk. But his mother had observed that his temper was very much disturbed. Moreover, his disposition was of that nature that, in the first place, he rarely yielded to passion but when he did yield, he was apt to lose his reason completely. She must beware lest in very truth he should burn up all the new clothes. She hurried to her daughter-in-law, and said: 'Daughter, for God's sake, don't do anything to spoil the happiness of this one day of the whole year! Get up, and have your bath and put on your new clothes.'

Mizájdár said: 'No, lady; I never bathe at this time. I will bathe later.'

But in the end, after many entreaties and protestations, the mother-in-law got her to bathe; and having dressed her hair, and put on her clothes, she had her set up like a bride before Muhammad Aqil came back.

When Muhammad Aqil saw what had been done, he was made happy again; and as he was starting for the Eedgáh, he asked Mahmúda what toy he should bring back with him for her from the bázár. Mahmúda said: 'Bring me a nice pretty book-rest—I will put my daily portion of scripture on it—and a tiny little box to hold my reed-pen and inkpot.'

Here Mizájdár called out of her own accord: 'And for me?'

Muhammad Aqil said: 'Whatever you desire I am ready to bring.'

Mizájdár said: 'Maize cobs, and water-chestnuts, and berries of the jujube-tree, and some roasted pease-pods, and a whole lot of oranges, a drum, and a tambourine—'

Muhammad Aqil burst out laughing, and said: 'What will you do with a drum and a tambourine?'

The silly Mizájdár replied: 'Play upon them. What else?'

Then Muhammad Aqil understood that, even at her age, the silly girl was just like infants without discretion, having no higher ideas

than those of eating and playing. All the pleasure he had experienced
at her having put on her new clothes was turned to dust, and in that
state of despondency he went to the Eedgáh.

No sooner was he gone than Mizájdár made a new move. She said
to her mother-in-law; 'Send for a doolie for me; I want to go to my
mother's house.'

Her mother-in-law said: 'Goodness me! What time is this for you
to go? It is only eight days since you came back from your mother's
house after four months' absence. And to go away on the very day of
the Eed is absolutely improper.'

Mizájdár said: 'I am feeling very agitated today. My heart is coming
up the wrong way. My old friend Banno, the daughter of Básu the
bangle-maker, is always in my thoughts.'

Her mother-in-law said: 'God help you, daughter! Was there ever
such a passion as you have for Banno? If you want her so badly as all
that, send for her to come here.'

Mizájdár said: 'Ah yes, you are a good hand at inviting when you
can't help yourself. If she was to be invited at all, you might have sent
for her yesterday to see me put on my new bangles.'

Her mother-in-law said: 'Goodness, child! how was I to know that
you would be tickled with the thought of her all on a sudden?'

Mizájdár said: 'Well, it's no good arguing. If you are going to send
for a doolie, send for it. If not, I will get one brought by dear little
Sulmati's father.'

Her mother-in-law said: 'Child! has your reason been smitten? You
have not even asked your husband's leave. If you go, it's your own
doing. *I* am not going to have my aged locks shorn off that I should
send for a doolie without my son's permission.'

Mizájdár said: 'Husband, indeed! and permission! What? Is no one
nowadays to go and see her parents on the Eed, or the Baqar Eed?'[6]

With these words, having procured a doolie through Maulan the
greengrocer, she was off, and at her own home in no time.

Shortly afterwards Muhammad Aqil came back from the Eedgáh.

---

[6]The other great festival of the year, instituted to commemorate the sacrifice
of *Ishmael* (not Isaac) by Abraham. Baqar is pronounced Buckur.

As he burst into the house he called out: 'Here, Lady! take your drum and your tambourine, and play upon them.' Then he looked round; everyone was silent. He asked his mother: 'What has happened? Is all well?'

Mahmúda said: 'Sister-in-law has gone away.'

Muhammad Aqil was overwhelmed with amazement, and said: 'Eh? How did she go? Where has she gone to? Why did you let her go?'

His mother answered: 'All on a sudden, without a word from anyone, she began saying: "*I* am going to my mother's." She would not listen to any of my remonstrances, but got Maulan to fetch her a doolie, and off she went. I did all I could to stop her, but it was no use.'

While she was speaking Muhammad Aqil stood quivering with rage. His first impulse was to go off at once to his wife's home and chastize the good-for-nothing woman, and with this idea he moved towards the door; but his mother, divining his intention, called to him as he was leaving. When he returned no answer, she said: 'Well done, son! well done! Here am I calling you, and you hear me, and give no answer! Is *this* all the respect which is left to mothers in this thirteenth century?'[7]

As soon as he heard this, Muhammad Aqil retraced his steps. His mother said to him: 'Tell me, at least, my son, where you are going in this heat. You have only just come from the Eedgáh, and are you going outside again? By my life, you will make yourself ill.'

Muhammad Aqil said: 'Madam, I am not going anywhere; only to the mosque to see the caretaker.'

His mother said: 'Don't be so silly, boy. I have not bleached my hair in the sun. What, Sir! do you dare invent stories to me? If you are going to see the caretaker, take off your jacket and scarf, and leave them here, and then you can sit in the mosque at your ease.'

Muhammad Aqil began to smile at these words, and his mother, taking his hand, made him sit down by her; and then, looking at his head, she said: 'Your hair has got full of dust from your going all that way to the Eedgáh and back. Lie down for a minute and put your head on this cushion, and I will make it tidy for you.'

[7]The year 1869 A.D., in which the story was written, corresponded with 1285–86 of the Hegira, of Muhammadan era.

In obedience to his mother, Muhammad Aqil lay down just for a little while; and Mahmúda, seeing him in that position, began to fan him. Partly from the fatigue of his walk to and from the Eedgáh, and now the pleasant cool air of the fan but, above all, the delightful sensation of his mother's kind hand wandering over his head—however it was, Muhammad Aqil went fast to sleep.

When he woke up the sun had begun its downward course, and his own anger of the morning, too, had abated. His mother said to him: 'Now, wash your hands and face, and then say your afternoon prayers. This time is getting short. When you come back, I will tell you what I want you to do.'

CHAPTER
III

✦✦✦

When Muhammad Aqil came back, after saying his prayers, his mother said: 'Now, I want you to go to your mother-in-law's house; and mind, I adjure you by my life not to create any disturbance or quarrel there.'

Muhammad Aqil said: 'In that case, don't send me there.'

His mother said: 'Nay, my boy; ask God for kinder thoughts. Heavens! what a cruel tongue you have! Whom else *can* I send to your own wife's house? See, here is a rupee, which I want you to give as an Eed present to your sister-in-law Asghari; and here is an eight-anna piece for your aunt's son. Miyán Muslim;[1] and you had better take half of the toys too. Mámá Azmat[2] will carry a tray of *siwaiyán*[3] and milk, and a basket of sweetmeats, and you must take her with you. Now, mind! not a word.'

Muhammad Aqil said: 'And the drum, mother, and the tambourine? Shall I take them, too?'

His mother said: 'Hush! that's enough. Be off, now, and don't say a word on the subject when you get there.'

In due course Muhammad Aqil arrived at his mother-in-law's house. Akbari khánam and her girl friends were playing high jinks inside, so

[1]Pronounce Meeyán Mooslim, the final 'n' of Meeyán like the French 'n' in 'rien', or 'viande'.

[2]Pronounce Uzmut.

[3]A dish resembling vermicelli, always eaten on the Eed. It is boiled without milk, but eaten with milk as oatmeal porridge is in England. The final 'n' of siwaiyán is pronounced like the French 'n'.

that the noise of their voices penetrated into the street. Mámá Azmat went inside.

As soon as Asghari caught sight of her, she said in a low voice: 'Sister dear! sister dear! be quiet; the Mámá from your husband's home has come.'

Azmat called out to Muhammad Aqil after she had gone inside: 'You may come in, young gentleman.'

Then Muhammad Aqil went into the house, and made his salaam to his mother-in-law, who wished him health and long life. Presently, Asghari also, having adjusted her veil, came out of her chamber, and, curtseying with the utmost grace, salaamed to her brother-in-law, who made her sit upon his lap and gave her the rupee. Asghari began to look towards her mother, but her mother said: 'Yes, you may take it; your brother-in-law makes you a present for the Eed.'

Asghari took the rupee and salaamed a second time, and then, getting off his lap, sat down at a respectful distance. But presently she got up again, and with admirable self-possession she spread a bright clean table-cloth in front of her brother-in-law, and then fetched a dish of *siwaiyán,* a jug of milk, a little plate of sugar, and a spoon, all of which she placed before him. His mother-in-law then invited him to eat. Muhammad Aqil excused himself by saying: 'I was late in returning from the Eedgáh today, and so it is but a short time since I had my meal.'

His mother-in-law said: 'What does that matter? *Siwaiyán* is not more substantial than water. Eat a little.'

While Muhammad Aqil was eating the *siwaiyán* Asghari made up a delicious *pawn*[4] with cardamoms in it, which she brought him. After his repast there was some general conversation. By-and-by Muhammad Aqil said: 'Your honor! I am ready to take leave.'

His mother-in-law said: 'Where will you be going now? You must sleep here.'

Muhammad Aqil said: 'Today is the Eed. There are visitors to be received, and, secondly, there are ceremonial presents to be seen to and despatched. Besides, I said nothing to my mother about staying for the night when I came away.'

[4]Pawn is chewed after every meal, being supposed to assist digestion.

His mother-in-law said: 'The time for receiving visitors has gone by now; it is nearly evening; and as for sending off the presents, your mother can manage that.' And then she laughed and said: 'You are no longer a baby; besides, Azmat will go back, and let your mother know.'

In fine, although Muhammad Aqil made many excuses, his mother-in-law would listen to nothing he said, and he was perforce obliged to remain.

An hour or so after nightfall, when the last meal of the day was over, Asghari put away the plates and the dishes, and whatever else there was lying about—all into their proper places. She chained up the door of the house, put the padlocks on the store-closets, and handed the keys to her mother; extinguished the lamps in the outer saloon and in the kitchen, provided enough pawn for her mother and sister and brother-in-law, and, having seen that everything was right, went off comfortably to bed.

Then his mother-in-law addressed Muhammad Aqil as follows: 'Now, my son, I want to ask you what are these daily quarrels I hear of between you two, husband and wife. Not that Akbari has said anything. It is a wretched habit of hers that she never by any chance lets me know anything about her new home. The custom of the whole world is for daughters to tell their mothers every little thing that goes on in their husband's family, but—however God has chastened her is a mystery to me—you may go on asking and asking her till your tongue is weary—don't expect *her* to say a word. Still, what is the talk of the mohulla does get round to one's ears somehow; and, sitting at home all day as I do, I hear a good deal from people who drop in.'

When his mother-in-law had finished speaking, Muhammad Aqil took some time for reflection. His sense of propriety made it difficult for him to frame an answer. But he thought to himself that, since the opportunity he had so long waited for had now arrived, and she herself had broached the question, it would be altogether inadvisable for him to be silent under the circumstances; that he had far better get rid once for all of the poison that had so long been brewing; and that possibly out of the present conversation some good result might arise for the future. Accordingly he replied, with much bashfulness: 'Your honor's lady daughter is present; will not your honor inquire from *her*

what annoyance she has been put to in our home—whether there has
been anything lacking on our part in courtesy or consideration for
her; whether anyone has quarrelled with her, or spoken unkindly of
her? Your honor is aware how many there are of us in the house to
count. My revered mother, the whole mohulla knows, is so great a
peace-lover that such a thing as a quarrel with anyone has never happened
to her in her life. Even if people so forget themselves as to speak rudely
to her she bears it in silence. Muhammad Kámil is engaged all day
long in his studies; when he has gone out in the morning he does not
return till the evening, and then has his supper and goes to bed. *I*
have never even seen him talking to her. Mahmúda is frightened by
the very sight of her. The only other person is myself, who am now
sitting in her presence. If she has any complaint to make of me, let
her state it frankly.'

On this his mother-in-law turned to address her daughter, and
said: 'Now *you*, my dear, speak out plainly whatever you have on your
mind. When a thing stays on the mind it does not improve. The longer
you keep it there the more it worries you, and its evil influences grow
apace.'

Now although Akbari was most audacious in lying, at that particular
moment, face to face with her husband, she could find nothing whatever
to say. Indeed, in her heart of hearts she was greatly alarmed lest the
many falsehoods which she had dinned into her mother's ears whenever
she came home should be summarily exposed. After much anxious
reflection, she evaded the real question at issue. All she could say was:
'What *I* want is a separate establishment.'

The mother said to her son-in-law: 'And *you?* What objection have
you to your living by yourselves? God be thanked! You have an
appointment. You earn your own living; you are not dependent for any
of your wants on your parents; you can feed yourself and clothe yourself.
What advantage is there in living under other people's protection?
Son, I tell you, however much a bride may be petted in her father-in-
law's house, she does not get the same comfort there that she has in a
house of her own, where she can eat when she wants to eat, and cook
what she wishes. And there is just this to consider: as long as you live
with your own people you may earn lakhs of rupees and get no credit

for it. Who is to know whether you are maintaining yourself or living on your parents' bounty?'

Muhammad Aqil said: 'If your honor makes the question one of comfort, then the value of the comfort which we actually enjoy will be appreciated after we have left our home more than it is now. We eat our meals ready cooked for us morning and evening, and have no anxiety to disturb our leisure. After we have set up house for ourselves there will be all the worry of thinking about the meal, the pulse, the meat, the vegetables, the fuel for cooking, and what not. Your honor knows better than I what a lot of worries there are in managing a house. And it does not seem to me that there would be much sense in anyone's bringing all these troubles upon himself without cause. What your honor says about the liberty of eating what we like, and cooking when we like—that is exactly what we enjoy now. Ask *her* whether she has ever expressed a wish for anything which has not been gratified. In large families, no doubt, this kind of inconvenience does arise. One person has a fancy for sweetened rice, while another wants browned *khichri*,[5] and a third demands *pulá-o*[6] and a fourth is bent on having *khorma*,[7] while a fifth has been prescribed a low diet by the doctor's order. Ten dishes for ten people every day are not forthcoming. But at our place there is no such big family. Who is there to bespeak anything but ourselves? or to object to anything except ourselves? However, let that pass. If she is so particular about it, let her undertake the ordering of the meals herself. My mother has often said as much; ask your daughter there whether she has not. And as for what your honor mentioned about the *name* of the thing, in my humble opinion that, too, is no sound argument. A man has to consider his own peace and comfort; other people may imagine what suits their fancy. But suppose people have arrived at the conclusion that I am living on my parents' bounty, what disgrace is there for me in that? They are my *parents*, not strangers. They brought me up, and gave me shelter and food and clothes, and had me educated, and provided me with a wife. In all

---

[5]A dish of mixed rice and pulse flavoured with burnt onions.
[6]Meat stewed with rice.
[7]Strong soup.

this I incurred no loss of honor. What red-goose-feather have I got in my cap now that my living under their protection should be supposed to be derogatory to my dignity?'

His mother-in-law replied: 'If everyone thought as you do, how is it that people *have* separate establishments? It is the custom of the whole world. It always has been the way, and always will be, for sons to leave their parents; and, whatever you may say I know for a fact that no bride whose husband earns his own living will be content to live with her mother and sisters-in-law.'

Muhammad Aqil said: 'What your honor says is perfectly true. If sons did not leave their parents' homes, how should there be so many houses in the city? But the case of every individual is different. In *my* case, living separately does not appear to me advisable from any point of view. True, I have an appointment, but only of ten rupees a month. To keep up a separate establishment on that income strikes me at once as very difficult. But there is no certainty about my appointment. God grant it be not so! but suppose I lost it after quitting my parents, it would be a great blow for me to come back again to them afterwards. *Then* I *should* feel some degradation, when people say: "Young master set up house for himself, but when he had played the fool long enough he came back to share his father's crumbs." Fashion is no safe guide in a matter of this kind. One must consider one's own circumstances. No doubt, your honor has heard the story how a man purchased a lot of salt and cotton in the market, and put the salt upon a mule's back, and the cotton upon a donkey. There happened to be a stream to cross on the journey home which was fordable, and the man drove the mule and the donkey, laden as they were, down into the water. When they were half-way across the mule dived, and as he brought his head up again some seconds after the donkey asked him: "Friend mule, what is this you have done?" The mule replied: "Brother, you may thank your good luck that you are laden with cotton, so light as it is to carry. I, poor wretch, am packed with salt, and my loins have got cut under the weight of it, so that they are streaming with blood. This master of ours is so unmerciful that he has not the slightest regard for our sufferings, but puts just as much as he likes upon our backs without considering the weight. I thought to myself, by the time we reach our destination my loins will be *nil*; suppose I take a dive. When the salt gets soaked, some of it, at least, will melt away. Whatever is lightened of it will be a gain to me. The master can but give me a few more blows of his stick, and, as it is, I get beaten all the way. See, now, my burden is only half what it was." The donkey, like a fool, was eager to follow the mule's example, and made a plunge into the water. The cotton became all the heavier for soaking, and, when he lifted his head out, he could hardly move. The mule laughed, and said: "Brother donkey, how fares it?" The donkey said: "Comrade, I am dying." "Oho," said the mule, "you *are* a stupid. You thought to follow my lead, but you might have known you had cotton on your back, and not salt." I do not wish, dear mother, to bring myself into the donkey's condition by following the fashion.'

His mother-in-law said: 'My friend, it is no use expecting you to agree with anyone, and I have never learnt logic, as you have. I only understand the plain fact that you are earning ten rupees a month. By God's grace, times are cheap, and you have no children. Two persons, husband and wife—God keep you!—can very well feed yourselves on bread and meat, and wear fine calico and muslin. If people worried themselves about the future as you do, the world would come to a standstill. Let alone your appointment, there is no *certainty* about your life. But the days that you have to live you may just as well pass cheerfully and happily.'

Muhammad Aqil said: 'That is just what I am debating in my mind, whether happiness is to be secured in living apart, or with my parents.'

His mother-in-law said: 'What is the object of all this puzzling and quibbling? Why don't you say straight out that you don't choose to leave your mother? Your wife has told you the one thing she wishes, and you make this tremendous demur in agreeing to it; and then you say that you never fail to consult her feelings. What *are* peace and happiness? Why, what makes your wife happy, and what she considers peace.'

After this a tone of bitterness began to be apparent in her remarks, and Muhammad Aqil deliberately kept silence. The night, too, was by this time far advanced. Muhammad Aqil said to his mother-in-law: 'Your honor had now better retire. I will think over the matter again.'

CHAPTER
IV

✻

While the people of the house were sound asleep, Muhammad Aqil spent the whole night long in revolving the question, and reproducing all the arguments for and against it in his own mind. In the morning when he got up, the first thing he noticed was that Asghari was sweeping the house. When she saw him she salaamed, and said: 'Honored brother, there is some warm water ready for ablution, if you are going to say your prayers.'

Muhammad Aqil said: 'No, my dear! I shall say my prayers at the mosque with the congregation.'

Asghari said: 'You won't go *away* yet, brother, will you? I have made some tea for you; but do you take it plain or with milk?'

Muhammad Aqil said: 'Just as you please.'

'Your voice seems rather husky,' said Asghari; 'perhaps it is the beginning of a cold, and milk will be bad for you.'

'No,' said Muhammad Aqil; 'I am not going to have a cold. I was up very late last night talking to your mother. I did not have a good night's rest certainly.'

Muhammad Aqil went to say his prayers, and when he came back he found his mother-in-law, who had finished her devotions, chewing pawn. He salaamed to her, and sat down.

Asghari brought in a small tray and laid it in front of him—hot tea in the teapot, two cups, two spoons, and sugar in a little bowl. The tea which he drank had a delicious flavour, and a lovely colour, and was as fragrant as you might wish. After drinking it he felt quite invigorated.

Akbari, according to her wont, was still in bed and asleep. Muhammad Aqil remarked: 'Mother, dear, I wish you would insist on *her* saying her prayers.'

His mother-in-law replied: 'Son, she was her grandmother's spoilt pet. It was her grandmother's fondness for her which ruined her temper, and her habits, and everything else. When she was quite a child, if I happened to scold her for anything, she would not speak to me for days together; and that anyone should dare to punish Grandmama's Akbari was quite out of the question. She would disobey every order; she would smash all the things in the house to bits; no one could say a word to her for fear of Grandmama. I was always getting into trouble with her father on that very account.'

Muhammad Aqil now prepared to take leave. As he was going, his mother-in-law said: 'Son, remember last night's talk, and be sure you make some arrangement to carry out our plan.'

All the way home Muhammad Aqil was haunted with this one thought. When he arrived, his mother saw there were lines of care on his face. She thought to herself: 'There has been a quarrel with his wife's people for certain.' She asked him: 'Well! did you disobey me, after all?'

Muhammad Aqil said: 'Believe me, mother, there was no kind of quarrel whatever.'

His mother said: 'Then what makes you so downcast?'

Muhammad Aqil said: 'Nothing. I came away directly I got up;[1] perhaps my face looks a little glum on that account.'

His mother said: 'Nonsense! as if I had not seen you just after getting up plenty of times. Tell me the truth; what is it?'

Having no alternative, Muhammad Aqil gave his mother a full account of all that had happened the night before. As she listened to him, she became so pale that it seemed as if no blood were left in her body. But she was a woman of a very philosophic temperament. She began saying: 'No doubt, it was my one desire that I should keep you all close to my own heart as long as there is any life left in this body, and that you two brothers should dwell together in fast friendship; but whichever way I look, all the chances seem dead against me. I tell you,

[1] *i.e.*, without making his usual toilet.

as sure as I sit here this very day, Mizájdár has been bent on having a separate establishment ever since the second month after the wedding: Your giving *me* the ten rupees you bring home every month annoys her to the last degree. Day after day I hear her girl friends talking about it. "The bride," they say, "is going to take a house in the Birdcatchers' ward;[2] she will take Zulfan along with her." This is the constant theme of their conversation whenever they are seated together. One day I said to her aunt straight out: "If Mizájdár does not like living as one of the family, let them stay on in our house, and arrange for their own food and clothing separately;" but I found out from her aunt that even that would not be acceptable to Mizájdár. People get married to be happy, and enjoy themselves. Can anything be worse than continual discord and daily quarrels? If nothing will satisfy your wife but a separate establishment, and she thinks *that* will make her happy, let it be so in God's name! I make no objection. Wherever you live, live happy and be prosperous! It is only this mother's fondness for her own offspring which God has laid upon my shoulders,—But you will come round now and again; I shall have a look at you, and be contented; or, sometimes, when I get a little leisure from the work of the house, I shall go round myself and see you.'

At these words, Muhammad Aqil's heart became full to overflowing. He could not restrain himself from shedding tears, and it seemed to him then as if he were already bereaved of his mother. She, too, wept. Presently Muhammad Aqil said: 'My wife may go or stay; I will not leave my own home.'

His mother said: 'Son, you do not know what it is you are saying. Are wives ever divorced in respectable families? It is with her that you will have to spend the whole of your life. And what is there left of me? I am only waiting with my feet hanging over my grave. My dying to-day will not prevent the sun rising tomorrow. My advice to you is to do just what she says. From the very day when I gave you in marriage, I knew you were parted from me. Neither you nor I are exceptions to the rule. What son has ever passed his life in his mother's house?'

Muhammad Aqil next consulted his own friends. They, too, all gave him the same advice, and said: 'The chief thing is to avoid any

[2]One of the best residential quarters in Delhi at the time.

scandal; and, as for your filial obligations, they are not bound up in your living at home. You may have your own house, and still yield to your mother the service and obedience which are her due.'

Finding that everyone gave him the same counsel, Muhammad Aqil, too, said to himself: 'Well, we will try how living separately does. If the girl will only come to her senses, and look upon her home as a home— if she will give up her bad temper, and disobedient ways, and rude language, living separately is no *crime,* there is nothing wrong in it. There will be all the worry of housekeeping, and we shall be badly off, that is all. But while one lives in this world, there is no freedom from care in any state of life. Say that, as it is, I am free from *care,* this daily strife of itself is a torture to me. Besides, it is not right to be overanxious about living on narrow means; whatever portion has been decreed to us by God's providence is certain to reach us in any case. There is no loophole in that for the labour or contrivance of man.'

Buoyed up by these considerations, Muhammad Aqil finally resolved to leave his parents' house.

It so happened that there was a house vacant close to his home. He got the landlord to agree to a rent of one rupee a month for it, and went so far as to pay entrance-money in advance, and sign an agreement. He then brought away the key, and sent a verbal message to his wife's home: 'A house has been arranged for; we can move into our new home as soon as you come.' And he said to his mother: 'I have taken the wire-drawer's house close by.'

His mother collected all the things belonging to Mizájdár bahu— the boxes of clothes, plates, carpets, mosquito-curtains, beds, whatever there was—and had them put into a separate room. In the evening, Mizájdár bahu herself arrived. Early next morning his mother unlocked the room, and said to Muhammad Aqil: 'Now, then, I want you both, husband and wife, to take stock of your things.'

Muhammad Aqil said: 'Mother, dear! what are you saying? As if it were a stranger's house!'

His mother said: 'I don't mean that, my son; but I don't want any of the things to get mixed up or mislaid in the moving of them.' Then she called the Mámá, and said: 'Azmat, do you and the woman next door carry over all these things to the wire-drawer's house.'

But by this time Akbari's comrades, Chuniya, Rahmat, Zulfan, and Sulmati, had arrived, and in less than no time they transferred all the things from the one house to the other. Mizájdár bahu entered upon possession with the utmost glee.

For three days Muhammad Aqil's mother sent over their meals morning and evening. On the fourth day Muhammad Aqil said to his wife: 'Now, Madam, I think you might begin to make some arrangements for our food.'

Mizájdár said: 'The things are all in disorder at present; when they are arranged I shall be able to look after the cooking at my leisure, but I have no time now.'

Accordingly, for seven days their bread[3] was baked in the baker's oven, and by sending to the bázár for kabábs[4] in the evening, and curds in the daytime, husband and wife managed to make their meals. At length, after harping on the subject every day, Muhammad Aqil induced Mizájdár to prepare a meal herself.

Now, Mizájdár had never done any cooking in her life. Her first chupattie[5] was of a marvellous appearance; neither round nor square; one corner sticking out here, and four corners there; the edges thick, the centre like a wafer; burnt on one side, not baked on the other, but all black with smoke. And the dál[6] was boiled so as to be half pulse and half water. In short, Mizájdár prepared a meal so delicious and exquisite that any appetite would be scared away by the very sight of it. And as for the sauce,[7] it was as nasty to look at as to taste. If she put any salt in, there was enough to kill one, and at other times it was a tasteless fluid. Muhammad Aqil exercised his patience for two or three days; after that he began to take his meals regularly at his mother's house. Mizájdár, too, consulted her own ideas of comfort, and used to make her meals off kachauris[8] and cream, or curds, or porridge, or kabábs, which she

[3]That is, they lived upon baker's bread instead of on the unleavened cakes called chupatties, which are ordinarily cooked every day at home.

[4]Bits of meat roasted on a skewer.

[5]A chupattie in shape and size resembles an old-fashioned 'pancake'. It is made of kneaded meal (not flour) and water, and eaten while still warm.

[6]Dál is made of split pulse boiled with clarified butter.

[7]The sauce (sálan) would be made of some green vegetable.

[8]Cakes fried in clarified butter.

obtained morning and evening from the bázár. Whatever she cooked herself was eaten by Zulfan and her tribe, who got fat upon it. These were the cats to whom 'Luck sent the larder.' But how were such luxuries possible on ten rupees a month? Silently and surreptitiously articles of furniture began to find their way to the bázár. Muhammad Aqil, however, was kept in absolute ignorance of this.

CHAPTER
V

O ne day, when Muhammad Aqil had gone off to his office, Mizájdár took a midday siesta. Chuniya happened to come in, and, finding her fast asleep, at once went off and told her brother Míran.[1] Now Míran was a thorough scoundrel, up to all kinds of villainy. While Mizájdár was still sleeping soundly, he entered the house in broad daylight, and carried off all her copper vessels. When Mizájdár got up at last, and looked round, the house had been clean swept. The things in the store-room, which were under lock and key had escaped; but, with that exception, he had taken away every single thing he could lay hands on. There was not even a cup left to drink out of. When Muhammad Aqil came back from his office, he was sorely grieved; but of what use was fretting now, *when the birds had left the field bare?* He quarrelled fiercely with his wife, and beat his own head soundly, but sobered down at last after much lamentation. By dint of raising money from his friends he bought two second-hand copper pans, and he borrowed some smaller vessels from his mother. A kneading-pan, a griddle, and a platter were sent by his mother-in-law, and so they managed to get on somehow or other.

It was just about this time that a female sharper paid a visit to the city, and created a considerable stir among all the inhabitants. Muhammad Aqil, like other people, took the precaution of warning his wife, and said: 'By no means allow any strange woman to come into the house.

[1]Pronounce Meerun.

There is a female sharper who has lately come here, and robbed several families.'

But Mizájdár was incorrigibly silly. It was a regular habit of hers to admit anyone to her confidence at a moment's notice.

One day the female sharper came into the lane on which Mizájdár's house abutted dressed up in the guise of a Hajjan,[2] for in that character the designing wretch used to carry about with her a lot of sacred relics and things of a hundred different kinds suitable for the purpose of hoaxing silly women, such as rosaries of the sacred earth of Karbala, and flasks of the water of Zamzam; dates from sunny Medina, and antimony from Mount Sinai; shreds from the black pall of the Caaba, beads of agate and coral, Nád Alis and Panjsúras,[3] and a whole quantity of drugs. When she came into the lane and spread out her articles for sale, a good number of girls collected round her. Mizájdár, too, heard of her coming, and said to Zulfan: 'As soon as the Hajjan is ready to go, make her come in here. I, too, would like to pay my respects to her sacred relics.'

Accordingly Zulfan went and stood over the Hajjan, and brought her back with her.

Mizájdár gave the woman a warm reception. She made her sit down by her side, and inspected all the things, out of which she selected two—viz., some antimony and a Nád Ali. The Hajjan had guessed from her conversation that Mizájdár was just the kind of woman to fall into her trap. She let her have the Nád Ali for two annas, and weighted her out quite a large quantity of the antimony for one pice; besides which she gave her a turquoise ring as a present for nothing. Mizájdár was enraptured.

Then the Hajjan told her all about the sea, and life in Arabia, and some things entirely of her own invention, but such that Mizájdár listened to them with consummate delight and regarded her with a special attraction. The Hajjan inquired of her: 'Lady, have you no children?'

Mizájdár said: 'No such luck as that for poor me!'

---

[2]Hajjan (pronounced Hujjun) is an Indian-made feminine of the Arabic Háji, a title given to a man who has performed the pilgrimage to Mecca.

[3]These are small tablets of stone inscribed with prayers or sacred texts.

The Hajjan asked: 'How long have you been married?'

'Not a whole year has passed yet,' replied Mizájdár.

The Hajjan was now fully convinced of Mizájdár's stupidity, and said to herself: 'Why, she heaved such a sigh when I mentioned the word children, as if she had been pining for them for years.' Then she said: 'There is no reason to be despondent; *you*—why, you will have more children than you will know what to do with. Just at present, no doubt, you feel depressed at being all alone in the house. What sort of a man is your husband?'

Mizájdár said: 'He is always displeased with me.'

In short, at their very first meeting, Mizájdár was so unreserved with the Hajjan that she told her anything she asked about herself; and with a little catechizing the Hajjan found out all her secrets. The Hajjan sat there fully three hours, and when she took her leave, Mizájdár besought her: 'Dear lady Hajjan, when will you come here again?'

The Hajjan said: 'I have a niece living in the Waxmakers' Buildings who is very ill. It was to nurse her that I came here from Agra. What with tending her, and giving her medicine, I don't get much spare time; but, please God! I will manage to look in and see you every other day or so.'

However, the very next day she presented herself again, and this time she brought with her a silk trouser-cord. Mizájdár was rejoiced to see her again, and asked: 'What is this trouser-cord for?'

'It is for sale,' said the Hajjan.

'How much is it?' asked Mizájdár.

The Hajjan replied: 'It is going for four annas. There is a Begam[4] living in the mohulla who has now become poor, and she has to sell her things, one after another, in order to live. I am in the way of selling lots of things for her.'

The mere sight of such a cheap trouser-cord made Mizájdár long to possess it. She got out the money in no time and gave it to the Hajjan, and said with great earnestness: 'Dear lady, whatever things there may be for sale, let me always have the first look at them.'

---

[4]Pronounce Baygum. The word means 'Lady' (of rank), and is the feminine of Beg, as Khánam is of Khán.

'Very well,' said the Hajjan; 'you first, and the rest afterwards.'

After this they went on talking on different subjects for some time. As she prepared to go, the Hajjan produced a little purse, inside of which, wrapped up in several folds of paper, there were a few cloves. She took out two of them, which she gave to Mizájdár, and said: 'Friendship exists in the world simply for this reason, that each one of us should be a help to someone else. I give you these two cloves. Tie one of them into your top-knot, and the other—it would be better if it could stay in your husband's turban, but perhaps he might suspect something—well, sew it into his pillow, and watch the effect of it from today. But take care of one thing; see that the place they are kept in is always clean and pure. And let me have a piece of yarn of the measure of your height; I will get a charm made of it and bring it you. When I went on the pilgrimage to Mecca, a great lady of Bhopál—perhaps you, too, may have heard her name, Balqís Jaháni Begam[5]—was a passenger on board the same ship. God had given her everything she could want. There was no end to her wealth; servants and officers, handmaids and pages, pálkis and nálkis[6]—every single thing but one. She had no child, and for that want she passed her days in sorrow. Moreover, the Nawáb, her husband did not trouble himself in the least to please her; and, maybe, it was on account of her having no children that he did not love her, for otherwise the Begam, as far as grace and beauty go, was *now the sun and now the moon;* and with all her beauty and riches she had a nature so simple as to let insignificant people like me sit opposite to her and be concerned about our welfare. The Begam had the greatest faith in Faqirs.[7] One day she heard that a very eminent saint was staying six miles off from where she was. She went all the way on foot in the middle of the night to visit him, and for three hours she stood in front of him with her hands clasped. You may stake your life on the fame of Faqírs! The great king, lifting up his eyes for one moment, looked at her, and said: "Go, mother; this night your orders will come." In her sleep there came the divine message: "Go to Mecca, and fetch up from the sea the pearl of your desire." As soon as she

---

[5]Pronounce Bulkees.
[6]Pálki and nálki are different names for what we call palankeen.
[7]Persons vowed to poverty; pronounce Fukeer.

woke she commenced her preparations for the pilgrimage. She took
with her on board ship five hundred poor persons whose passage she
paid for, and of these I was one. Constantly with her as I was, the
Begam sáhib (god make her face bright in both worlds!) began to treat
me with great kindness, and used to address me as "Comrade." Ten
whole days the ship moved over the waters. On the eleventh day there
appeared a great mountain in the middle of the sea. The Captain said:
"This is Abyssinia, and on that mountain there dwells a very eminent
Faqír. Whoever goes to him obtains the wish of his heart." The Begam
said to the Captain: "Set me down upon that mountain at all costs."
The Captain said: "Your highness, the ship cannot sail close to the
mountain; but if it be your pleasure, I will anchor the ship and take
you there in a boat." The Begam said: "Be it so then." Five women
went with the Begam to the Abyssinian mountain—myself, and four
others. When we reached it, a wonderful fragrance filled the air. On
we went till at last we reached the great king.[8] It was an awful spot.
No man, nor any child of man, save the great king alone, dwelling in
a cave. And what a splendid apparition! like an angel of light. Looking
upon all of us, he pronounced a blessing. To the Begam he gave twelve
cloves, and after reciting some words, he breathed upon her. To me
he said: "Go, make people's business prosper in Agra and in Delhi."
Daughter, out of those twelve cloves these are two. When we returned
from the pilgrimage, we found that the Nawáb, who at one time
never even asked after the Begam's health, had been waiting—mark
the difference!—a whole month in Bombay for the express purpose
of receiving her. As soon as she stepped on shore he laid his head at her
feet, and with the utmost contrition entreated her forgiveness. I stayed
at Bhopál for six years after we returned; and before I left, through the
Faqír's blessing, the Begam already had four sons (god keep them!),
one after another, without a break. At last I remembered my own country,
and asked the Begam's permission to depart. She did all she could to
keep me, but I said: "*The King* enjoined me to serve Agra and Delhi.
Go there I must." When she heard that, the Begam had no choice but
to let me go.'

[8]That is, the Fukeer. The title Sháh is commonly applied to saints.

Two cloves, and a lovely romance of four pages in addition! Mizájdár was converted, heart and soul. The Hajjan left the cloves and took her departure. Mizájdár had a bath, changed her clothes, scented herself, and, with a prayer to God, tied one of the cloves into her top-knot. Then, after changing the sheets and pillow-cases of her husband's bed, she placed one clove inside one of the pillows.

When Muhammad Aqil came home, he found his wife clean and nicely dressed, the bed with clean sheets on it, without a word from himself. He was delighted, and began talking to his wife with genuine affection. Mizájdár said: 'See, I have bought something today;' and she showed him the trouser-cord.

Muhammad Aqil said: 'What did you give for it?'

She replied: 'You must guess that. How much is it worth?' Now, the trouser-cord was of real Lahore make, and extremely fine; broad, and thick woven; and with knotted tassels of silk and gold thread. Muhammad Aqil said: 'Certainly, it is not worth less than two rupees.'

Mizájdár said: 'I got it for four annas.'[9]

'No,' said Muhammad Aqil; 'you are joking.'

Mizájdár said: 'I swear by your head, I got it for only four annas.'

Muhammad Aqil said: 'It is very cheap. Where did you pick it up?'

Mizájdár said: 'There is a Hajjan who comes into the lane, and had done so for a long time—a most excellent woman. The trouser-cord belongs to some Begam, but *she* brought it for sale.'

And then Mizájdár showed him the antimony, and the Nád Ali, and the turquoise ring.

So evil a thing is covetousness, that the very wisest of us are apt to be beguiled by it. Even wild animals—the maina, the parrot, the amadavat, the nightingale, who fly away at man's appearance—still, from greed of the scattered grain, allow themselves to be caught in the net, and pass their whole lives shut up in a cage. In the same way, when Muhammad Aqil saw some profit for himself, he was delighted; and on Mizájdár's telling him that the Hajjan had made her a promise to bring her all the things which the Begam might give her to sell, he replied: 'Certainly,

[9]At the time of the story two rupees were worth four shillings, and four annas equalled sixpence.

you ought to see them. Only take care they are not stolen goods; that would mean ruin hereafter. And, another thing, are you quite sure the Hajjan is not an imposter?'

Mizájdár said: 'Ask God for pardon! The Hajjan is not one of that sort.'

And so the matter ended.

From the pleasant way in which her husband conversed with her on this particular day, Mizájdár's faith in the virtue of the cloves was confirmed. The next morning she sent Zulfan to invite the Hajjan to her house, and that day she treated her as a mother, and behaved herself like a daughter to her. In the evening she spoke of the Hajjan again to Muhammad Aqil, and again he said: 'Look out; be careful. There are numbers of bad characters who adopt this disguise.'

But covetousness had cast such a film over Muhammad Aqil's own common sense that he quite failed to consider the very obvious question: 'Does anyone give two-rupees' worth of property in exchange for four annas without some good reason?' By rights, Muhammad Aqil should have put a stop once for all to the Hajjan's coming to the house, and he should have had all her things returned to her forthwith. As for Mizájdár, she had not the sense to fathom such deep problems.

CHAPTER
VI

A few days afterwards, Mizájdár asked the Hajjan how it was she had left off bringing any of the Begam's things. The Hajjan perceived that she had swallowed the bait, and said: 'If anything in your style turns up, be sure I will bring it.'

Two or three days after this she brought a couple of false pearls with her, and said: 'See, lady; these pearls belonged to the Begam's own nose-ring. Heaven knows if the pair of them are worth a thousand rupees or five hundred. As I passed Panna Mal[1] the jeweller's shop, I showed them to him. He was simply dazed with them, and would have made me take two hundred rupees for them by force. I brought them from the Begam to sell for fifty. *You* take them. You won't get such a chance again.'

Mizájdár said: 'I have not got fifty rupees in cash.'

The Hajjan said: 'What does that matter, child? You can sell your wristlets and buy them, or else—you may take my word for it—they will be sold this very day.'

The Hajjan said this with such an air that Mizájdár immediately brought out her jewel-box, and taking out the wristlets, made them over to the Hajjan. *She* was looking at Mizájdár's jewels the while, and said: 'Dear me! how carelessly you have stowed away your jewellery, as if it were a heap of carrots or radishes! Daughter, why don't you have the beads of your necklace threaded! And here are your earrings,

[1]Pronounce Punna Mull.

and all their appurtenances, and your armlets, too, all soiled with dirt. Dirt, you know, eats into the gold. Why don't you have them properly burnished?'

Mizájdár said: 'Who is there to get the beads threaded? and who would go and have the things burnished for me? If I ask *him*, he says he has no time.'

The Hajjan said: 'Oho, daughter! that is no great business. See, let the pearls stay here; I will get the necklace threaded in a minute; and if you will pick out the ornaments which are dirty, I will get them burnished for you at the same time.'

Mizájdár made over all the jewels to her. The Hajjan said: 'Send Zulfan with me, too. She can stay by the goldsmith while I am getting the string put in by the silk-worker.'

'All right,' said Mizájdár; and she called Zulfan.

When Zulfan came, the Hajjan said: 'My good girl, I want you just to come with me and wait at the goldsmith's shop.'

Then she took the jewels, and Zulfan accompanied her.

When they got out of the lane the Hajjan undid the handkerchief, and said to Zulfan: 'Suppose we put the things to be burnished on one side, and the pieces to be threaded on the other.'

All on a sudden, as she was sorting the jewellery, the Hajjan exclaimed: 'Eh! where is the nose-pin?'

Zulfan said: 'It will be among the lot; it is but a tiny little thing; look into this bag.'

Then the Hajjan cried out of her own accord: 'Oh! of course, it was left behind lying on the lid of the casket. Run, Zulfan, quickly and fetch it.'

Zulfan came running back, and shouted out at the door: 'Lady, the nose-pin was left behind in the lid of the casket. The Hajjan has sent me for it. Give it to me quickly; the Hajjan is at the corner of the lane, sitting in front of Dibyá the banya's shop.'

At these words Mizájdár's forehead began to throb. She said to Zulfan: 'Have you gone mad? What pin? Did I ever have one? Have you ever seen it? Bad luck to you! run off at once, and see that the Hajjan does not get away.'

Zulfan took to her heels, and ran back again. She looked about everywhere for the Hajjan, but there was no trace of her. Then she came back, and said: 'Lady, I cannot find any trace of the Hajjan, though I looked for her all the way to the bázár. Goodness knows where she has vanished to, all in a minute.'

When she heard this, Mizájdár began to beat her head and cry out: 'Help, help! I am robbed, I am robbed! Run, good people! for God's sake run!'

The neighbours did run all the way to the Waxmakers' Buildings. There they discovered that some stray woman or other had been living in a hired lodging for the last month, but had given it up and gone away four days previously. What was to be done now?

Muhammad Aqil heard the news when he came home. He beat his head, and said to his wife: 'Oh, you woman! you'll bring the house to utter ruin before you have done with it. I know what sort you are, from the very beginning!'

Mizájdár said: 'Get away with you! out of my sight! Do you stick yourself up to scold me *now*? When you saw the trousercord, did not you say yourself, "Yes, you should certainly have a look at the Begam's things"?'

And so there began a highly-delectable quarrel between the two, husband and wife, which drew all the people of the mohulla together. When they came to compare notes it was found out that this same Hajjan had cheated the wife of Ahmad Bakhsh Khán, in the Kanchani[2] lane, out of all her jewels by saying that she would get them doubled in weight by a Faqír. And the same woman had struck up such a friendship with Miyán Masíta's daughter, in the cotton market, that she had carried off all her jewels on the pretence of borrowing them. In short, the jewels were dead and gone, but plenty of gossip survived them.

All Mizájdár's cooking utensils had already been stolen, and now she was similarly plundered of her jewels. When they examined the two pearls valued at a thousand rupees they were found to be worth three pice. Information was lodged at the police-station, and many private inquiries were made by the neighbours but all in vain. Nothing more was ever heard of the Hajjan.

[2]Pronounce Kunchunee.

Would you like to hear what happened to the clothes which Akbari got in her marriage trousseau? As long as she lived in her mother-in-law's house, her mother-in-law used to take them out and air them in the sun once in every ten or fifteen days. It was in the rains that Akbari set up house for herself. Her box of clothes—it never had a chance of being looked at all through the rainy season—was allowed to remain in the same room, exactly as it was when it was stored away. As winter came on a quilted wrapper happened to be wanted, and then the box was opened. A quantity of the clothes had been eaten by white ants. Rats had gnawed some, and made great holes in them. There was not a single dress which had entirely escaped.

It is always the case. Girls who are perpetually being coddled and indulged when they are little, and who are taught nothing that is useful or practical, invariably reap trouble and sorrow throughout their after-lives, just like Akbari. From all that you have read about her, you will, I think, have formed some idea of how much misery the petting of her mother and grandmother entailed upon her during her whole life.

In her girlhood Akbari did not learn a single accomplishment, nor were any faults in her temper corrected. When she left her mother-in-law's house to set up for herself, everything had been provided for her—plates, and dishes, and clothes, and jewels. But as she had no practical knowledge of housekeeping, in a short time she let the whole of her possessions go to rack and ruin and within a single year she was left without an ornament either for her wrist or her ear. If Muhammad Aqil had been equally foolish and bad-tempered, very likely they would have been separated from each other for ever. But Muhammad Aqil throughout adhered to the dictates of reason and the honor of his family.

CHAPTER
VII

❧

Now listen to the story of Asghari. This girl was to her family what a rose in full bloom is to a garden, or the eye to a human body. Every kind of acquired excellence, every kind of natural intelligence was hers. Good sense, self-restraint, modesty, consideration for others—all these qualities God had bestowed upon her. From her childhood she had a distaste for romping and jesting and ill-natured jokes. She loved reading, or doing the work of the house. No one had ever seen her chattering rubbish, or quarrelling with anybody. All the women of the mohulla loved her as they did their own daughters. Blessed indeed was the fate of those parents who owned Asghari for a daughter! and happy was the lot of that family into which Asghari was now to be admitted as a bride!

At this time, by the grace and favour of God, Asghari's age was fully thirteen years. Her betrothal had already been settled, and now there began to be a talk of fixing the day and the month. But on her side, Muhammad Kámil's mother, after her experience of Akbari's ways, had become so frightened—according to the proverb, 'He who has burnt his lips with milk[1] blows his butter-milk before drinking—'that her hair stood on end at the very thought of her. She had privately set her mind upon getting her son betrothed elsewhere. But Muhammad Aqil by some means got to know of this, and said to her: 'Mother, I have

[1]In India milk is boiled as soon as it is obtained from the cows, and is often drunk before it has had time to cool thoroughly.

heard that you wish to break off Muhammad Kámil's engagement; is that so?'

His mother said: 'What can I say, my son? I am in great perplexity what to do, and what not to do. As for you, I am ashamed to look you in the face; God has made me such a sinner against you. See, now, what kind of fate is in store for Muhammad Kámil.'

Muhammad Aqil said: 'Mother, believe me, Asghari is one girl out of a thousand. You may take a lamp and search all your life long, and you will not find any girl like her. In outward form and inner nature alike, God has placed her in the foremost rank of His creatures. Do not have the least misgiving, but set about the preparations for the wedding in God's name. And if you are thinking about her elder sister—well, perhaps you have heard the saying of the Persian poet:

> Not every lady is a *lady*, nor every man a *man*.
> God has not made the five fingers all of one pattern.

Everyone has a different constitution, and everyone a different type of character:

> Flowers in plenty, rich and rare,
> Bloom in the garden everywhere.
> Each has a hue none else may share,
>   Each has a fragrance all its own.[2]

"There is no power nor might, save in God;" but what comparison is there between your eldest daughter-in-law and Asghari?

> The dust has no alliance with the pure sky.

God prosper us! after the marriage you will realize the truth of what I say.'

As a result of Muhammad Aqil's speaking so strongly in praise of Asghari, her betrothal with Muhammad Kámil once more became valid; so that, by the common consent of both parties, it was now agreed that the marriage should take place with due solemnity on the day after the Baqar Eed.

Asghari's father, Dúrandesh Khán, held a Government appointment in the Hills. Formal intimation was sent to him. On receipt of the letter

---

[2]The lines in the original are from a poem by the last King of Delhi.

the Khán sáhib was highly delighted, for, of all his children, he was fondest of Asghari. He immediately submitted an application for leave, but it was summarily refused, and all the efforts he made to overcome the resistance were fruitless. The cold weather was approaching, inspection duties were just beginning, so that his superior officer had reason on his side. Dúrandesh Khán was much grieved at not getting his leave, but—'in service one is helpless—'what could he do? 'The poor man's wrath hurts only the poor man's soul.' He resigned himself to his lot in silence. But he had with him his eldest son, Khairandesh Khán. Him he sent home with a sum of 500 rupees, and careful instructions about every detail of the ceremony.

The jewels, clothes, copper vessels, and things of that kind, were in the house all ready in anticipation of the event. When Khairandesh Khán arrived, he made purchases of rice, ghee, wheat, spices, and salt, according to their requirements in each article. The extra trimmings began to be sewn on to Asghari's dresses. It was her mother's desire that Asghari should receive a trousseau considerably in excess of that supplied to her elder sister; that her costumes should be more heavily embroidered, her jewels more in number, and the cooking utensils for her use of greater weight in copper. Of course, anything of this kind could not altogether escape Asghari's knowledge, for, after all, she lived in the same house. When she found out that she was likely to have a larger trousseau than her elder sister, if she had been a silly girl she would have been pleased. Asghari was greatly vexed, and yet quite at a loss for some device by which she could manage to dissuade her mother. At last, with much diffidence, she addressed herself to Tamásha Khánam, her first cousin on the mother's side, to whom she mentioned what she had heard, and said: 'For several days I have been saying to myself, "Good heavens! what shall I do?" I am so glad you have come round in the very nick of time. I don't mind speaking to you, because we are of the same age. Someone or other must just tell my mother not to give me anything in excess of my sister.'

Tamásha Khánam listened to her, and said: 'Well, sister, I must say you are an extraordinary woman. Why, it is the old saying, *They gave salt to the donkey, and he said, "I have sore eyes"*. God bids you take it; why do you refuse?'

Asghari said: 'Have you gone mad? There are several reasons against it. You know my sister's disposition; she is certain to be annoyed. It will create in her a bitter feeling against our mother for no purpose. It will make her suspicious of me also.'

Tamásha Khánam said: 'What ground is there for her annoyance in this, my dear? Every girl has her own luck. And there are a hundred ways of accounting for it. She had a feast at her *bismillah*,[3] her first fasting was kept, her betrothal lasted for four years; what annual ceremony was omitted then? She can find a balance there for any deficit on this side of the account.'

Asghari said: 'True, but there is something in the *name* of a trousseau. If a younger sister gets more, the elder *must* be annoyed. Besides, living in the same mohulla, meeting each other every day—why *should* anything be done which will cause a breach between two hearts?'

Tamásha Khánam said: 'My dear, you are damaging your own interests for no earthly good. Why, in a month or two, she will have forgotten the whole thing.'

Asghari said: 'God pardon you! what are you saying? Is it a question of loss or gain? And does one ever stop at the *totals* of what parents give? And then a trousseau lasts one's lifetime. God grant you are not going to persist in this! If so, I must take some other steps. Nothing will induce me to approve of it.'

The end of it was that this conversation came to the knowledge of Asghari's mother, and she, too, after some reflection, abandoned her project. She said to herself: 'There are a hundred ways of giving; I can make it up in some other quarter.'

Well, on the appointed day, at an auspicious hour, the marriage ceremony was performed. Congratulations and good wishes followed. Khairandesh Khán was such an excellent man of business that he managed everything single-handed with the greatest success. The guests, all of them according to their rank, were treated with the most punctilious courtesy. All the people who were entitled to *bakhshish* were amply satisfied. When the time came for Asghari to leave her home there was quite a commotion in the house. Her mother, as you

[3]When she was first put under a governess to be taught reading.

may suppose, felt her departure to be a calamity of the first degree. The ladies of the mohulla were so affected that they came, each of them repeatedly, and placed their arms round Asghari's neck and wept. Blessings from the heart were uttered by all of them. Laden with a trousseau, rich, indeed, of these blessings, Asghari passed into her father-in-law's home.

There all the ceremonies which are customary in the bridegroom's house were duly performed. After the unveiling of the bride, the title of Tamízdár[4] bahu was given to Asghari Khánam.

In the sequel you will learn how Asghari sustained the burden of housekeeping, what difficulties she encountered, and how they vanished before her common sense. But now, just compare the two cases of Asghari and Akbari. Asghari was her mother's second daughter, and her mother-in-law's second daughter-in-law. On both sides the hopes and ambitions of the family had already been lavished upon Akbari's wedding. Akbari was married at the age of sixteen, and Asghari at the time of her marriage was barely thirteen. When Akbari was married, her husband, Muhammad Aqil, already had an appointment of ten rupees a month, but Asghari's bridegroom, Muhammad Kámil, was still studying. By comparison with Muhammad Aqil, Muhammad Kámil had less knowledge and less natural ability. Akbari remained free from the cares and troubles of a family for two whole years, whereas God made Asghari a mother in the second year of her married life, while she was still of a tender age. It was never Akbari's lot to leave the city, but Asghari spent years of her life away from home. Thus, in every way, Asghari's case, in comparison with that of Akbari, was not a favourable one, *save only* that Asghari in her childhood had received a good training, and day by day its blessed influence continued to grow within the family circle. To such an extent, that at this date no one knows Akbari's name, but in the Khánam bázár there is Tamízdár's mansion, so lofty that it seems to hold converse with the sky, and the mohulla itself is called Khánam bázár, after Asghari Khánam. The big mosque in the Jauhari bázár,[5] in which there is a bathing-place and well, was con-

---

[4]Pronounce Tumeezdar; the word means 'having discretion.'
[5]Pronounce Jowharee; *i.q.* Jewellers' Street.

structed by Tamízdár bahu's orders. Tamíz ganj, near the Lál diggi,[6] after you pass the Kháss bázár,[7] is her property. To this day, twenty poor strangers get leavened bread and dál broth twice a day from her kitchen attached to Maulavi[8] Muhammad Hayát's mosque. The Sarai at the Qutb,[9] alongside of the Auliya[10] mosque, owes its existence to her. At Fattihpuri, 500 copies of the Bombay edition of the Qur-án were distributed by her in one day. And even now a thousand blankets are given to the poor every winter from her house.

[6]A tank faced with red stone.

[7]*i.e.*, the quarter occupied by tradesmen to the royal family of Delhi.

[8]Pronounce Mowlavee

[9]Pronounce Kootub, the name of the famous minaret in old Delhi, about eleven miles from the present city.

[10]Pronounce Owliya. The word means 'saints'.

CHAPTER

VIII

When Khairandesh Khán announced to his father Dúrandesh Khán that, 'By the gracious favour of god, my dear sister's marriage was solemnized with every circumstance of felicity on the eleventh day of the month Zilhijja, the dowry being that of the blessed Fátima,'[1] Dúrandesh Khán performed two obeisances of prayer as a thank-offering. But grief at the thought of his severance from his daughter haunted him for many a long day. The letter which he wrote to Asghari after her marriage is worth perusing. A copy of it happened to come into my possession. It runs as follows:

'Ease of my heart and soul, my daughter Asghari Khánam! May God Almighty send her peace! After my blessing, and a yearning to kiss your eyes, be it known to you: I have received the account which your brother Khairandesh Khán wrote to me of your departure to your new home. It had been my heart's desire for years that this function should be discharged under my own personal supervision, but since the Government would not give me leave, I had no choice in the matter. It can hardly have escaped your notice that out of all my children I have been particularly drawn towards you; and I do not write this as claiming

---

[1]By 'dowry' is meant that which the husband settles upon his bride, and to which she would be entitled in the event of a divorce. With the view of checking divorces, the practice has arisen of making the husband promise more than he would be able to afford. But this practice is condemned by the more religious, who follow the precedent of the Prophet when he gave his daughter Fátima to Ali. The sum fixed in her case was ten dinárs, equal to about 100 rupees.

any gratitude for myself; on the contrary, it is you, who by your own helpfulness and cheerful obedience, have secured a place—not in my heart only, but in that of everyone. Since you were eight years old, you have taken the whole burden of my family upon your head. I have always realized that the Begam (I mean your mother) has been saved a vast deal of anxiety through you. And whenever I have happened to go home on leave within these years, it has rejoiced my heart to notice your excellent management of the house.

'I learnt also from Khairandesh Khán's letter that you were unwilling to accept a larger trousseau than Akbari's. This shows your disinterestedness and generosity, but the letter I am now sending you is a *quid pro quo* which may please you better. Keep it by you as a rule of conduct, and if you act up to the instructions contained in it, please God every difficulty will become easy to you, and you will pass your lifetime in peace and tranquillity.

'I wish you first to consider what marriage is. A marriage is not merely the putting on of fine clothes, and the assembling of guests, and the getting presents of furniture and jewellery. No; but marriage is the beginning of a new world. You have to deal with new people, and live in a new home. It is as when for the first time two young bullocks have a yoke put upon them; this yoke for the scions of the human race is marriage. As soon as the marriage ceremony has been performed, a girl has become a wife, and a boy has become a husband. This means that the pair of them have been caught and yoked to the cart of the world. Henceforth they have to drag that cart together to the final resting-place of the grave. It is evidently better for them that they should submit themselves to pull this heavy burden with stout hearts, and that they should spend the days of their life's journey, be they few or many, with dignity and self-respect, in perfect amity and concord. For what is the alternative? Angry quarrels and disputes and bickerings and clamorous upbraidings and lamentations only make the world's hardships ever more and more distressing. Now, my dear daughter, Asghari Khánam, I want you to consider how great a difference God has placed between husband and wife. It is written in the books of our religion that the patriarch Adam, when he was alone in paradise, was ill at ease, and that God created our mother Eve, who was the first woman in the world, to solace him. Hence the creation of woman was merely to insure the happiness of man, and it is woman's function to keep man happy. It is greatly to be regretted that so few women in the world fulfil this task. God has given to man a somewhat higher status than to woman—not only by His command, for He has also given to men's bodies greater physical strength, and to their mental faculties a greater perspicuity. All the control of the world's affairs is effected by men. They are the *workers* who earn money by their toil, and women are the *guardians* of what men have earned, and spend it from time to time to the best advantage. A family is like a boat, and the men in it like sailors. If there is no sailor in the boat, it will either founder in the waves, or be dashed to pieces against the shore. If there is no man in a family capable of managing it, every kind of mischief may be apprehended.

'Do not for an instant suppose that happiness in this world is obtained from wealth and large possessions. Although there is no doubt that wealth is often a cause of happiness, yet in many great and wealthy families I find strife and misery prevailing beyond measure. Happiness in domestic life arises solely from unanimity and goodwill. I see poor men, whose income is of the smallest, earning their living by severe toil all day long, and at night their family, all seated together, appease their hunger with bread and pulse, and are happy and contented one with another. Without a doubt these people, by reason of their kindly feelings for each other, are better off with their bread and pulse, and their coarse and scanty clothing, than the Nawábs and Begams, whose luxurious living is throughout embittered by their selfish antagonisms. My dear Asghari Khánam! cultivate unanimity, and count the greatest prize in domestic life to be mutual kindness.

'And now, consider by what means unanimity is to be secured. It is not enough by itself that a woman should *love* her husband; in addition to love, she is bound to show him respect. It is great folly in a woman to suppose that her husband is on the same level with herself. But worse than that: in these days women have adopted a horrible attitude which is altogether subversive of good manners. When half a dozen of the sisterhood are sitting gossiping together, the talk is generally about what kind of treatment "So-and-so" expects from her *husband*. One says, "Sister,

I have subdued him to that extent he never dares to interrupt me or answer me back." Another makes her boast, "I never touch my food until he has coaxed me for ever so long." A third clenches her superiority by saying, "When he asks me the same question ten times over, I barely mutter an answer." A fourth chimes in, "He may sit on the floor for hours together, your humble servant makes a point of not leaving the sofa." And a fifth sums up her importance with the remark, "Whatever my tongue utters, I get done to my liking, or else I leave him." And all the charms and spells that have been invented for marriages have but this one object—that the husband should remain humble and obedient to his wife's orders. Some collect lamp black upon the sole of a shoe, and use it for the husband's collyrium; that means that he is to get shoebeaten all his life, and never say a word. Some make up a pawn, and put it under the great-toe when they are bathing, and afterwards give it to the husband to eat, that means that he is to be always at her feet. It is clear enough from such practices as these that women are on the alert to lower the dignity and authority of men; but this doctrine is a very evil doctrine, and its result will never be free from evil. God has given to men a nature like that of tigers; whoever tries to tame them by force and domineering will find it impossible. A very simple receipt for taming them is being agreeable and submissive; and every silly woman who aims at bringing her husband under subjection by the violent assertion of her own authority makes a great mistake. She is sowing the seeds of strife from the very beginning, and, though she may not think so at first, strife will inevitably be the ultimate result. My advice to you, my dear Asghari, is that you should make a point of treating your husband with respect, even in your conversation and demeanour.

'Again, why is it that weddings are celebrated with such exuberant rejoicing, and yet after the fourth day there begins to be ill blood between the bride and her mother and sisters-in-law? Here is a question which demands anxious consideration. All the time before marriage the boy is under his parents' authority, and his affections are centred in them alone. His parents have brought him up, and cherished the hope that in their old age he will minister to their wants. *After* marriage the bride, from the very moment that she sets foot in the house, begins manœuvring in order that her husband may quit his parents' home at once. Thus, the quarrel always originates from the side of the bride. If she would make herself at home in the family, and not let the mother-in-law feel that she is trying to rob her of her son, no trouble whatever would arise. Everyone knows that after marriage the parents' hold upon their son is but temporary; sooner or later he will leave them, and the young couple will set up house for themselves; it always has been so in the world. But brides (bad luck to them!) have such an impatient spirit—Heaven knows how—that whatever is to be must be *this very moment.*

'One common fault of brides, which causes a lot of mischief, is tale-bearing. I mean that, whenever they go home to their mothers, they report every little thing that takes place in their mother-in-law's house; and their mothers also are only too apt on their part to question them on such matters. But nothing comes of all this asking and telling, except that ill-will is engendered and quarrels arise. Some brides are so supercilious that, however good the food and the clothes may be which they get in their mother-in-law's house, they look upon them with contempt. Naturally the husband is mortified by such conduct. I trust that you, Asghari, will be very circumspect in this matter. You can find out *some* merit in everything at your mother-in-law's house, and you ought to show your cheerfulness visibly after eating your meals or when you put on new clothes, so that people may know that you are pleased with them.

'There is another thing which a new bride should be careful to remember in her mother-in-law's house—namely, not to give way to low spirits the whole time she is there. Although one does not always feel at ease among strangers, from the very fact of not knowing them still, you should try to command your feelings, and not, as they say, "went there crying, stayed there crying; no sooner gone than she longed to come back." The bride's periodical visits to her mother[2] are an excellent institution for helping her gradually to form new ties; but to exhibit a constant yearning for the mother's home, in excess of that custom, is sure to be resented by the bridegroom's relations.

'In your conversation let the golden mean be your rule; that is to

---

[2]For some time after the wedding the bride pays visits to her mother at fixed intervals by an arrangement between the two families.

say, do not be so forward as to be constantly prattling apropos of nothing, nor so backward that your silence should be put down to pride. Incessant chattering often results in causing pain to somebody; for where there is such a propensity, a thousand different subjects of discourse will crop up, and who knows in which of them what words may escape your lips? And yet you ought not to preserve such a reticence that people should be driven at last to entreat and beseech you just to say something.

'Contrariness and obstinacy in any matter are not becoming. Even if anything should happen which offends your taste, let it pass at the time; you will be able to deal with it satisfactorily at some other opportunity. Do not dictate your own desires in any matter; by doing this, people lower themselves in the eyes of others, and their words lose their effect. Do not think it beneath you to do with your own hands any work in the house which your mother and sister-in-law are in the habit of doing. Kindness to your juniors, reverence to your seniors— that is the cardinal maxim for ingratiating yourself with all. Do not shift any work of your own on to the shoulders of others, and do not leave anything of your own lying about for others to pick up. When two persons are talking together in a low voice, withdraw yourself from them, and do not trouble your head about what they were saying; above all, do not jump to the conclusion that it was you whom they were talking of. In your intercourse with those of your own age, be prudent and reserved at the first start. People who form intense friendships with great alacrity are always liable to take offence with equal rapidity. It is my wish that you should read this letter through every day, even when there is no necessity for it, so that its purport may always be kept in your view. And now God bless you! Written by Dúrandesh Khán.'

CHAPTER

IX

The receipt of her father's letter produced a burst of emotion in Asghari's loving heart of no ordinary kind. She would gladly have given way to tears, but as a newly-wedded bride, in her mother-in-law's house, that was impossible. She exerted all her powers of self-control, and, after pressing her father's letter to her eyes, she placed it very carefully in her book of daily lessons, and made it her practice to read it and meditate upon its contents regularly every day.

In the earlier days of her wedded life Asghari did feel very ill at ease, as was only natural after suddenly quitting her mother's house to live among entire strangers. She had become inured to a life of constant activity and supervision; she could not bear to be without employment for a quarter of an hour. And now she was condemned to sit demurely, confined to one room, with nothing going on, for months together. The liberty which she enjoyed in her parents' home was no longer hers. As soon as she arrived in her mother-in-law's house, everyone was intent on watching her, and scrutinizing her every action. One scans her features; another appraises the length of her hair; another guesses her height; another examines her jewels; and another takes stock of her clothes. If she eats anything, each morsel is observed. What sized bit did she take? How wide did she open her mouth? How did she masticate it? And how did she gulp it down? If she rises from her seat, they look to see how she robes herself in her mantle, how she holds up her skirts. And if she sleeps, they count the hours; what time did she go to sleep? When did she get up? In short, every phase of her deportment was under observation.

All this was terribly distressing to poor Asghari; but since she was endowed with common sense and a good education, she emerged with credit even from this ordeal, and her manners in general were approved of by her husband's relations. When she talked, it was not to such an extent as that people should say, 'Bless the girl! only married four days, and she keeps up such a tremendous rattle!' nor was she so sparing of her words as to be set down as surly and ill-tempered. At her meals she did not eat so much as to be the talk of the mohulla, nor so little that her mother-and sisters-in-law might be tired out with pressing her, and she take no notice of them. She did not retire so early that it was a case of, 'As soon as the wick was in the lamp, so soon my darling was on the couch;' nor did she lie in bed so long that you might suppose she was sleeping for a wager against the dead.

It is in the order of things that a new bride is besieged by all the young girls of the mohulla. Asghari, too, might have seen surrounded by half a dozen of these at any time. But Asghari exhibited no partiality in respect of any of them. If a girl sat with her the whole day long, she did not say, 'Sister, must not you be going home now?' And if any one of them had missed coming, she did not ask, 'Where were you, sister? How is it you did not come?' Under this method of entertainment and manner of complaisance adopted by her, the crowd of girls gradually became smaller, and especially those of the lower classes in the mohulla, who were actuated by cupboard love; when they found there was nothing to be got out of her—and no talk of sly purchases from the sweet-shops—in five or six days they dispersed like foul humours, and left her alone.

The first person whose friendship Asghari cultivated was her sister-in-law Mahmúda;[1] and since Mahmúda was but a child, she was easily won over by a little attention. All day long she was at Asghari's elbow; indeed, her mother sometimes exclaimed, 'How is it you are so fond of this sister-in-law? You used to run away from your elder sister-in-law's shadow.' And Mahmúda would reply, '*She* used to beat me; my dear younger sister-in-law loves me.' From Mahmúda's society Asghari reaped no small advantage. In the first place, she gradually learnt all

[1]Pronounce Mehmooda.

the history of the household, nay, of the whole family, and even of the
mohulla. And then, if there was any matter which from shyness or
etiquette as a new-comer she could not mention herself, she made
Mahmúda her mouthpiece. It was in this way that she began, by degrees,
to take part in the work of the house. At evening time she would ask
Mahmúda for some cotton, and twist the wicks for the lamps. She
would prepare the vegetables for cooking. She would mend any of
Mahmúda's clothes that were torn or had come unstitched. She would
prepare the pawn for her mother-in-law and her husband. As time
went on, she penetrated even into the kitchen, and gave Mámá Azmat
some hints about the way to fry and to brown, until at last the meals
were regularly cooked under her advice. As soon as Asghari began to
have a finger in the cooking, the inmates of the house made the
discovery that food too is a marvellous blessing. After a while it was
the fact that, if by any chance Asghari was not at hand to look after
Mámá Azmat, the dishes that day would go round untasted.

The feuds between mothers-in-law and daughters-in-law have
become a by-word. Since Asghari was incapable of quarrelling, her very
accomplishments became the cause of ill-will. Mámá Azmat had
acquired such a right of occupancy in the house that she was now
the pivot upon which everything turned. All the purchases for the
household—clothes, grain, whatever came from the bázár—passed
through her hands. Even the family jewels were entrusted to her for
repairs or alteration; and if any loan was required, it was raised through
her agency. In short, Mámá Azmat ruled the house, as if she had been
a man. Directly Asghari's influence penetrated as far as the kitchen,
Mámá Azmat's peculations began to be discovered. One day a dish of
minced *kabábs* was being cooked, and Asghari, sitting in the kitchen,
was giving Mámá Azmat directions. When the meat was ready minced,
and it was time to add the curds and spices, Asghari said to the Mámá,
'Let me taste the curds; if they are stale and sour, the *kabáb* will be
spoilt.' The Mámá brought out the cup of curds, and gave it to Asghari.
When Asghari tasted them, they were as sour as sorrel leaves; they
had been kept for days, and were resolved into blobs of matter floating
in a greenish liquid. Asghari said: 'Oh dear! what horrid curds! These
will never do to put into *kabábs*. Be quick, Mámá, and go and fetch

half an anna's worth of good curds, and see that they are sweet and fresh.'

The Mámá said: 'Lor', madam! what good will half an anna's worth of curds be for two pounds of meat?—"a carroway seed in a camel's mouth." These curds you disapprove of cost an anna.'

Asghari was amazed at this, and said: 'Why, at home we had *kabábs* nearly every day, and always for two pounds of meat we used one and a half pice worth of curds. At that rate, I asked you to get two pice worth[2]—thinking it rather more—so that the *kabábs* should be particularly juicy and brown.'

The Mámá said: 'Lady, you just leave the reckonings of your mohulla alone. Where is the Chandnee Chowk, I should like to know? and where is the Turkoman gate?[3] What costs a pice there, you cannot get for an anna here. This God-forsaken mohulla is "a ruined township with its barren land." All the year round there is nothing but loss, nothing but scarcity.'

Since the dinner was being delayed, Asghari listened to this in silence, and only said to the Mámá: 'Well, fetch it at once, whatever the price may be.'

But she was not so simple as to accept the Mámá's explanation. She said to herself: 'There is "something black in the dál" here, for certain. A difference of a few cowries would be no great matter, but when it comes to *twice* and *four times* the price, in two mohullas of the same city, it is scandalous.'

After this Asghari was on the look-out. Next day the Mámá brought in some pawn-leaves. When Asghari saw them, she said: 'Mámá, you always manage to bring home light-coloured leaves; there is no taste nor flavour in these. Now that the cold weather is commencing, you ought to look about for well-grown and mellowed leaves to bring home.'

The Mámá said: 'Mellowed leaves are selling at two for a pice; and in this family (God protect it!) the consumption is half a bundle a day. That is why I bring young leaves.'

---

[2]There are four pice in an anna, and three *pics* in a pice.

[3]The Chandnee Chowk is the main thoroughfare in Delhi, at one time famous over all Asia. The Turkoman gate is the name of a mohulla on the outskirts of the city.

Just at this moment Asghari's own Mámá, Kifáyat Nisá,[4] came in from Asghari's home to inquire after her. The question of the pawn was still under discussion. Asghari turned to her own Mámá, and said: 'Kifáyat Nisá, at what rate are you buying pawn now?'

Kifáyat Nisá said: 'Sixteen for the pice, Lady.'

Asghari opened her desk, and, putting two pice into Kifáyat Nisá's hand, said: 'Go and get some from a pawn-seller of this mohulla.'

Kifáyat Nisá went, and brought back forty large, thick, succulent leaves.

Asghari said: 'Why, you have got four more in the pice than even in the Chandnee Chowk!'

Kifáyat Nisá said: 'Lady this mohulla is the gate of the city. Whatever comes into it comes by this approach. Meat, grain, pawn—all these things can be bought cheap in this mohulla. Fresh vegetables, indeed, which come from the Sabzimandi,[5] enter the city by the Kábuli gate. Very likely they are a little dearer. I got old leaves at forty; if I had taken young leaves, I could have had sixty.'

Asghari said: 'This good-for-nothing Azmat sets fire to everything alike. Kifáyat Nisá, I wish you would stay here for two or three days. I will send a message to my mother. Anyone can look after the work there just for a day or two.'

Kifáyat Nisá said: 'Here I am, lady, at your service; God deal better with us! are you and yours two families?'

For four days the purchases of all kinds from the bázár were made through Kifáyat Nisá, and in everything there was conclusive evidence of Mámá Azmat's dishonesty. But this was all managed in such a way that Asghari's mother-in-law had no inkling of it. Asghari knew of it, or Kifáyat Nisá, or Mámá Azmat. For Asghari was a woman of great generosity and regard for the feelings of others, and she thought to herself, 'What is the use of bringing an old servant like her into disgrace and contumely?'

---

[4]Pronounce Kifáyut, with accent on the second syllable, and Nissa. The name means 'economy among womankind.'

[5]Pronounce Subzee Mundee: a village outside Delhi inhabited by market gardeners. Pawn-leaves are grown only on special soils, and under mat houses. They used to be sent distances of 300 or 400 miles by relays of foot-runners.

One night, after she had finished supper, Asghari was sitting on the flat roof of the house chewing pawn. Kifáyat Nisá, too, was seated near her. Mámá Azmat happened to come up. Kifáyat Nisá spoke to her and said: 'Say, sister Azmat, what goings-on are these? Every servant makes her pickings; no one denies that. Look you, the mistress of the house is present whom I served for seven years on end. She had the entire management of the house—and a rich man's house, too; God keep it so!—and a rich man's expenditure. Thousands of rupees' worth of purchases have been carried home in these hands of mine. The regular percentage of course I took; why deny it? We servants think *that* our duty, whether God pardon us or punish us for it, eh? But anything *beyond* that one cannot digest. Going further amounts to treason.'

Azmat said: 'Sister, is there anyone who does not know all about me? Do you think I care to conceal it? Granted, I steal and I plunder. It is nothing new; I have always done the same. But please to consider how I am placed—what a tremendous amount of work there is in this house. Inside and outside I am the only person. The work of four servants falls upon me single-handed. I tell you, sister, one does not give one's bones to be crushed in this way all for nothing. The mistress has dismissed me before this several times over, but she always had to send for *me* again in the end. It is the way in which you look at a thing; one looks at it one way, and another another. If I am here all by myself in the place of four servants, I ought to get the wages of four servants all to myself.'

Now, the fact about Mámá Azmat was this: she had been in the family for twenty-five years, and the whole of that time she had been intent upon plundering it. A thing which happens once can be hushed up, but in her case some fraud or other was discovered every day. She had been turned out of the house repeatedly; the instant she was dismissed the banya,[6] the cloth-merchant, the goldsmith, the butcher, the greengrocer—everyone from whom any purchases had been made by her upon credit—came to the house, and stood there dunning for their money. To be rid of this horror, she was always sent for again. Thus it was that theft and impudence alike were inscribed in Mámá

---

[6]Pronounce bunnya; a corn-seller and money-lender.

Azmat's lines of fate. She would take things before your face, and let you know she was robbing you. She would show you a thing, and make away with it, and have it written down, and then deny it. The income of the family was small, and their habits extravagant. Their food must be of the best, their clothes suitable to their rank. The whole establishment was kept going on borrowed money, and Mámá Azmat was the agent in all the negotiations. Hence the doors of the keep were open. She used to say, 'Turning *me* off is no easy business. Before I leave, I will have the house sold up; and if I go, it will be to the tune of falling bricks.'

When Asghari began to try and check the accounts, Mámá Azmat became her deadly enemy, and her one thought was how to make mischief against Asghari with Muhammad Kámil and his mother; but Asghari had no notion of her design, and, in fact, when she saw that Azmat was all-powerful in the house, and that there was no chance either of her mending her ways or of her being turned out, she said to herself, 'Well, in that case, what is to be gained by useless nagging! and why should I make myself objectionable to the Mámá for nothing?' And accordingly she left off going into the kitchen and interfering with the food altogether.

The inmates of the house, however, had got to know the taste of Asghari's handiwork by this time, and immediately began to make wry faces. One would say, 'Dear me! the meat is all gritty, like dust in the mouth;' and another, 'There is salt enough in the dál to kill one; my tongue won't stand it.' But no one dared to say to Asghari, 'Won't *you* cook the dinner?' Whatever Mámá Azmat served up to them, they were forced to eat, good or bad, just as she had cooked it.

CHAPTER

X

✦

One day in the rainy season—there was a thick mass of clouds overhead, and tiny, tiny drops of rain were falling amid cold gusts of wind—Muhammad Kámil said: 'I should so like a *karhá-í*[1] today, but only on condition that Tamízdár bahu superintends the cooking.'

Now, Asghari spent most of her time upon the roof;[2] she had not the slightest notion that Muhammad Kámil had expressed a wish for the *karhá-í*. Mámá Azmat went out and procured the ghee, the sugar, the gram-flour, and other ingredients, and said to Muhammad Kámil: 'Here you are, young master; I have brought in all the purchases. Shall I go now, and summon the lady bride?' Then she went up on to the roof, but she did not so much as mention the *karhá-í* to Asghari; she came down again without a word, and reported: 'The bride says she has got a headache.'

Mámá Azmat herself could not cook an ordinary dish decently; what earthly chance was there of her cooking a *karhá-í*? She served up the ingredients all messed together and utterly spoilt. Muhammad Kámil had been looking forward, I can't tell you how much, to his wish being gratified. After eating his nasty meal, he was proportionately disappointed. When he went up on to the roof, he found his wife engaged in sewing

[1]A 'karhá-í' means originally 'a large stew-pan,' and has become the name of a particular kind of stew.

[2]The roofs of Indian houses are flat, and surrounded by a parapet, so that women can enjoy the air without violating their privacy.

a pair of paijámas[3] for herself. He felt aggrieved, and said to himself, 'Eh, she is not too ill to be sewing, and yet when I asked for a *karhá-í*, she made the excuse of a headache.'

This was the first time that Muhammad Kámil had ever been annoyed with his wife, and it is just from petty little things like these that ill-feeling between husbands and wives ordinarily arises. Since marriages usually take place at a very early age, it follows, by God's grace, that sweet counselling reason is to be found neither in the husband nor in the wife. If either of them has taken offence at any little thing, you find the husband sitting sulking by himself, and the wife by herself lying on the sofa with her face averted. Considering that they have to live together, always in the same place, what wonder is it if very trifling matters in which they disagree with each other are of constant occurrence? But this antagonism, increasing with every instance of its repetition, produces in time a great collapse in their attachment and mutual friendship. Deference and loyalty disappear on either side, and the two pass the rest of their lives as if they were walking with peas in their shoes. The safest plan is for husband and wife to preserve their intercourse with each other unclouded from the very commencement, and not to allow even petty grievances to be formed; for otherwise, out of the accumulation of these petty grievances a huge amount of ill-will and misery is eventually created. And the secret of preventing any grievance from being formed is this: whenever anything occurs, however small, which gives you offence, not to bury it in your mind, but to speak it out face to face, and get clear of it. If Muhammad Kámil had known of this maxim, and been possessed of common sense, he would infallibly have taken his wife to task, and asked her *why* she could not do such a little job for him, but must needs tell a lie, and plead a headache. In that case the whole business would have been settled at once by a few words, and Mámá Azmat's roguery would have come to light. But Muhammad Kámil put a seal on his lips, and inscribed a whole volume of complaint upon his heart. Muhammad Kámil's coldness of manner made Asghari alarmed. She thought to herself, 'God help us! here is the beginning of a quarrel in prospect.' When she saw her mother-in-law, she found her

[3]Pyjamas—*i.e.*, trousers.

too looking gloomy. She was still more amazed at this, and said to herself, 'Good Heavens! what can it be?'

But before this matter could be explained, Mámá Azmat had aimed another blow. It was near the Ramazán. Muhammad Kámil's mother said to Mámá Azmat: 'Mámá, the Ramazán is coming on; you must begin at once to make preparations. All the copper vessels, big and little, want tinning; it is a whole year since the house was whitewashed. Tell Hazári Mal,[4] the banker, that he must manage somehow or other to let me have fifty rupees, since all the expenses of the Eed are falling on my head.'

Mámá Azmat said: 'Tamízdár bahu will be invited to her mother's house, and I have heard the Tahsildár,[5] too, is coming home; of course, he will send to fetch both his daughters. Besides, I did hear somewhere that it is Tamízdár bahu's intention to go back with her father; if she goes, no doubt the young master will go too. In that case, lady, you will be all alone in the house; what will you want with whitewashing? and what good will it be to have the vessels tinned? As for Hazári Mal, bad luck to him! He has got so crusty that his man waits at the door every day dunning for his money; how should he lend any more?'

When Muhammad Kámil's mother heard this, she was chilled to the heart, and the facts were enough to make her so. From the day when her husband went to Lahore he had not returned even to see what his home was like. Once in six months—once in a year, when he happened to think of it—he used to send her a remittance; but, except for that, he had ceased to trouble himself about her. Muhammad Aqil, as we have seen, had left his mother. The only one who remained to keep the house going was Muhammad Kámil. After *his* departure, the prospect was blank.[6] She asked the Mámá abruptly: 'Eh! Tell me the truth; are you sure Tamízdár bahu will go?'

The Mámá said: 'Lady, as to her going or not God knows; I only told you what I heard.'

Muhammad Kámil's mother asked: 'Eh? Bad luck to you! From whom did you hear? How was it discovered?'

[4]Pronounce Huzaree Mull.
[5]*i.e.*, Asghari's father, a (subordinate) 'collector'.
[6]Lit, 'the horizon was clear.'

The Mámá said: 'How did I come to hear? Well, I asked Kifáyat Nisá to lend me two rupees, and she said she would let me have them, but she was likely to be going to the hills. Then I inquired all about it, and found that everything had been settled to a "T". They are waiting till the Tahsildár comes—that's all; the morning after the Eed all these folk will start off. And why wait for hearing? "Though God be unseen, man's reason discovers Him." Do you mean to say, Lady, that you draw no conclusions from Tamízdár bahu's own proceedings? Don't you see how she used to be always looking after the housework at first, and now one would think her under an oath never to come down from the roof. Letter after letter is despatched to her father's address. What other business is there between them of such importance unless it be her going away?'

After this talk Muhammad Kámil's mother was left in a state of consternation, and she was still sitting wrapt in thought when Muhammad Kámil came home. She called him to her, and said: 'Kámil, I have something to ask you; will you promise to tell me the truth?'

Muhammad Kámil said: 'Goodness, mother! is there anything I should be likely to conceal from you?'

His mother then repeated to him word for word all that she had heard from the Mámá.

Muhammad Kámil said: 'Mother, I tell you truly that I have no knowledge whatever of this, nor has Tamízdár bahu ever mentioned the subject.'

His mother said: 'Go away, you hypocrite; do you try to impose upon me? A matter of that importance, and you to know nothing about it!'

Muhammad Kámil said: 'Well, if you won't be convinced, I swear by your head that I know nothing about it.'

Just then the Mámá, too, came in. Muhammad Kámil's mother said: 'How is this, you Azmat? Kámil says he knows nothing about it.'

The Mámá said: 'Young master, you may like it or lump it; your lady is making her preparations to go. Very likely she is keeping it dark from you. *She* is no Mizájdár, who could keep nothing to herself; this is Tamízdár bahu, who lets no one into her secrets.'

Muhammad Kámil's mother then asked him: 'Well, Kámil, if this thing should be true, what do you intend to do?'

Muhammad Kámil replied: 'Why, you don't suppose it possible, do you, that I should go away and leave you all alone? And Tamízdár bahu too—it is altogether out of the question that she should go away without saying anything or asking permission. I shall inquire of Tamízdár bahu this very day what is the meaning of it all.'

His mother said: 'Can we trust this wretched Mámá's words? Don't say anything to your wife about it as yet; when we are quite certain, we will see.'

By tricks of this kind, Mámá Azmat hoped to render Asghari obnoxious to her mother-in-law and husband; and, although neither of them said anything about it to Asghari in so many words, yet even she could not help perceiving from their looks that there was some embarrassment. In Mahmúda, Asghari had an admirable scout on her side. From little things that Mahmúda told her, Asghari gradually unravelled the whole of Mámá Azmat's villainy. But Asghari was not so silly as to give way at once to idle resentment; the conclusion she came to was that it would be unbecoming for her to initiate any discussion upon the subject; for, after all, the truth would be known some day, and then she could trust herself how to act. In her own heart she said: 'Just you wait a bit, Azmat; please God! even you shall see how smooth I will make you. Your brains have taken such a high range now that you think to set the whole family at enmity with each other. Please God! I will smite you where no water is,[7] and I will so cast you out that never again shall any luck bring you into this mohulla.'

[7]A proverbial expression for taking a person at a time when he can make no resistance.

CHAPTER

XI

Mámá Azmat's evil genius was now well astride of her. She delivered a third blow at Asghari. It was Hazári Mal's custom, whenever he saw Azmat passing by in front of his shop, to call out to her in a fussy way, 'How now, Mámá! have you any thought of paying my account?' and once a week or so he would send some dunning message to the house. One day, when Mámá Azmat was on her way to the bázár to make her purchases, as usual, Hazári Mal hailed her.

Mámá Azmat said: 'Lála![1] what new custom is this you have adopted of molesting me? Whenever you see me, you begin dunning *me*. Why don't you ask those you lent the money to? They are the people to dun. What have I, poor wretch! a lone woman, with two pice a day to live on—what have I to do with great bankers' accounts?'

Hazári Mal said: 'What's that you say? Nothing to do with it! *You* take the money from the shop. "The hand knows the hand." It is you, whom I know, and it is on your assurance that I lend the money. What do I know of the people of the house?'

The Mámá said: 'Oh, Lála, stop that nonsense; you are not such a born fool as that. What did you ever see in *me* to assure you? I have no lands; I have no money. And you have given me hundreds of rupees with your eyes shut! Well, if you gave them to *me*, go on, and get them

[1]The meaning of 'Lála' is something equivalent to the slang term 'Duckie!' but it has long since become a term for addressing men of sedentary occupations, such as money-lenders and shop-keepers and clerks.

from me. Sell up my mansions—wherever they are standing. Stop the issue of my pension from the palace—if I have any.'

Hazári Mal was quite taken aback at the Mámá's outburst of temper: He endeavoured to pacify her by saying, 'It seems that you have had a quarrel with someone today before you came out. Tell me what it is. Has your mistress said anything? or has the young master been angry? Come in, won't you?' And while he spoke thus to the Mámá, he put a pice into the hand of the boy who was looking after the shop, and said: 'Run and get two leaves of pawn made up, with some dry tobacco in them, and bring them here at once.' Then, when the Mámá was seated, he said to her again, with a laugh: 'You have certainly been quarrelling with someone; that is plain enough.'

The Mámá said: 'God forbid! Why should *I* begin to quarrel? You spoke, and I answered accordingly. When a thing is true, why do you take offence at it?'

Hazári Mal said: 'Sure enough, my *account* for the money is with the master; but does it pass through your hands, or does it not? I have neither note nor receipt; whatever you asked me for in your master's name, I gave you.'

The Mámá said: 'Yes, stick to that; when am I likely to deny it? I will vouch for whatever I have taken before any number of people; and my mistress too (blessings on her from every hair of my body!), she, poor dear! never disputes anything.'

Hazári Mal said: 'You are right there, Mámá; the Begam sáhib is a most noble lady. Bless her! there is no doubt of that.' And then in a low voice he asked: 'Tell me about the young bride; what is *she* like? Is she of the same complexion as her elder sister, or of a different disposition?'

The Mámá said: 'Don't ask me about her, Lála. The girl is of a noble family—true; but she is very stingy at heart. Even a farthing's worth of anything she won't approve until she has returned it four times. Ah, yes, in talent and accomplishments, God keep her! she is far ahead of most married girls. Her cooking is better than the best, and in needlework she could beat professional tailors and Mughlánis.[2]

[2] *i.e.*, women servants maintained by rich families to do fancy needlework and embroidery. The word is an Indian made feminine of Mughal, our 'Mogul'.

But oh, Lála! she is not what you call *well bred*. At first she began to fuss and meddle even with me. *You* know, Lála, how spotless my work is. She soon got tired of that. As for the Begam sáhib, *she* is a saint; it is the saving grace of her life and conduct that keeps the family going. And we unfortunate creatures only hold on to her skirts. People have often tried to frighten the Begam about me, but—God keep her in peace! her heart was never clouded. She never took in a word of all their talk against me.'

Hazári Mal said: 'I have heard the young bride had a very grand trousseau.'

Before he had finished speaking, the Mámá said: 'Rubbish! Not so fine even as the elder one's.'

'That is very odd,' said Hazári Mal; 'the Khán sáhib was a Tahsildár, too, when *she* was married. He ought to have given her more than the elder sister.'

'Ah,' said the Mámá, 'but it was not the fault of the Tahsildár. He, poor man! had made grand preparations. It was this little ill-bred pretender; she made them cut the items down, one after another, on the score of consideration for her parents, to win their favour.'

Hazári Mal said: 'If that is the case, she, too, will be wanting to keep house for herself, like her elder sister.'

'Keep house for herself,' said the Mámá; 'she will make bigger roses blossom than that. The elder sister was ill-tempered—no doubt of that; but she was open-hearted; and this girl is smooth-tongued, but she is not sound at the core. One may wear out one's life in working for her, and give no satisfaction. And whatever she will *say* to you, be sure there's something more at the bottom. Her words mean one thing, but her heart purposes something else. No, my little father, this girl is not the one to get on with anyone for a single day. At this moment she is making her arrangements to go to the hills, to her father.'

'Has any letter come from Lahore lately?' asked Hazári Mal.

The Mámá said: 'A letter is expected every day, but for some reason or other, I don't know why, none has arrived yet. The mistress is casting about to find money for the house. It was only yesterday or the day before she was saying to me, 'Go and get a loan of fifty rupees from Hazári Mal.'

At the word 'loan' Hazári Mal started back, and said: 'If she could find out some way to pay the old debt—*then* I would not mind lending again; but my partner won't hear of it now. You tell the Begam sáhib, Mámá, and see that she understands you; she must pay up the old debt, whatever she does, or else—don't let her blame me.'

The Mámá said: 'Well, if *God* should get your money out of them for you, you will get it. How is the Begam sáhib to pay? She is in debt, every hair of her. The cornfactor is worrying her life for *his* money, and the cloth-merchant is crying out to get his.'

'What have I to do with her other creditors?' said Hazári Mal. 'The Begam sáhib will have to pay my firm's account, anyhow. Personally, I have a great regard for the Begam sáhib's dignity; but my partner, Chidámilál, does not agree. If he were to hear what you have just said he would institute a suit this very day.'

The Mámá said: 'Well, I will repeat all this faithfully to the Begam sáhib. But I know every single thing about the family. You may bring a suit, or go into court, if you like. There is no money to pay, nor the means of raising any. If there were any money, why should they be asking for a loan?'

After the conversation had reached this point, Mámá Azmat took leave of Hazári Mal. When she got home at last with her purchases, Muhammad Kámil's mother asked: 'How now? Mámá, when you go to the bázár, you let your thoughts run so that you forget all about cooking the dinner! Can't you see how late it is? At what time will the meat be put on the fire? When will it be cooked? when shall we get our dinner?'

The Mámá said: 'Lady, the delay was all in arguing with that scoundrel Hazári Mal. The wretched creature has taken to stop me every day as I pass by. Today I fired up, and said to him: 'Why do you make it a rule to treat me every day to this insolence? What puts you in such a fright? Have a little patience. Let the remittance come from Lahore; then all your account from first to last will be paid off.' The creature made at me, and began wrangling and abusing me in the broad street.'

Muhammad Kámil's mother said: 'What has come over Házari Mal? He was never like that before. He has kept our accounts for years, and sometimes we have paid him early and sometimes late. He has never made any difficulty.'

The Mámá said: 'Lady, some other banker has become a partner in the firm. *He* has made this to-do about getting the debts in quickly, the wretch! He has been realizing straight off from all the clients, and those who did not pay he has filed suits against. Hazári Mal told me to say to you, with clasped hands, on his own behalf, that he had no voice in the matter; and to ask you to find some way of paying the money within two or three days, however you can manage it. Or else Chidámilál will file a suit for certain.'

Muhammad Kámil's mother was terribly disconcerted at hearing this news. There was, indeed, a younger sister of hers, Amír[3] Begam, living in the Khánam bázár, who was tolerably well-to-do in the world. Muhammad Kámil's mother said to the Mámá: 'No answer comes from Lahore, Mámá; not even a letter. What hope is there of any remittance? If Hazári Mal should really file a suit, what can be done? Even the furniture of the house in my possession is not sufficient for me to meet the debt with—if I should sell it. And then the mere fact of paying after a suit has been filed is a disgrace. Our reputation will be damaged all over the city. Go and fetch a doolie. I am going to Amír Begam. Perhaps some plan will be discovered there.'

The Mámá said: 'Lady, the suit is as good as filed. When a man has said a thing with his lips, it does not take long for him to do it. And where is the young Begam sáhib to get money from? She is embarrassed herself nowadays.'

Muhammad Kámil's mother said: 'Anyhow, something must be done.'

The Mámá went up to her, and said in a low voice: 'If Tamízdár bahu were to lend you her *bracelets,* just for one month, then the business might be put off. By pawning the bracelets only for the time, a half or a third of Hazári Mal's money would be made good. Within the month, either the master might send a remittance, or I could get you the money from some other banker.'

Muhammad Kámil's mother said: '*What!* are you mad? Take good care you don't let such a proposal pass your lips again. Should the house we live in be put up to sale, I would accept even *that*; but I have not the face to ask my daughter-in-law.'

---

[3]Pronounce Umeer, with the accent on the last syllable.

The Mámá said: 'Lady, it was only that I thought she is your daughter-in-law—you may say daughter—no stranger; and I had no intention—God forbid!—of selling outright. Just for a month—well, the things are not in her jewel-box; they are deposited with the banker. She might be perfectly at ease in her mind.'

Muhammad Kámil's mother said: 'Yes, but still there is a great difference between a daughter and a daughter-in-law. And a newly-wedded bride, too. Could anyone even mention such a thing? Take care, and don't let such a thing cross your lips again. Why, fancy, if it were to come to Mahmúda's ears, and she should go and tell her sister-in-law!'

The Mámá said: 'The young lady was standing here just now, and listening. But *she* is a child. What does she understand about such things at her age?'

Muhammad Kámil's mother said: 'Go and fetch the doolie. At all events, I will go to my sister. We shall see afterwards what plan we can arrange for the best.'

CHAPTER
XII

Muhammad Kamil's mother got into her doolie and departed to the Khánam bázár, and Mahmúda went off and rehearsed the whole conversation to Tamízdár bahu. Only one course seemed open to Asghari. She sat down at once and wrote the following letter to her elder brother, Khairandesh Khán:

'To his excellency, my gentle brother, the honored, the revered, health and peace! After my benedictions, I make known to you an urgent request, as follows: For a long time I have not written anything about myself to your honor, because I felt sure that the communications which I have in duty addressed to my honored father would also pass under your eyes. But now a special matter has arisen, of such a kind that I think it proper to be made known to you in particular. It is this: since I came to my father-in-law's house, I have experienced no kind of annoyance; and those matters about which my elder sister used to complain—through your prayers, nothing of the kind has happened to me. Everyone treats me with affection, and I myself am happy. But at the hands of one Mámá Azmat alone I experience such annoyance as would not befall me from a cross-tempered mother-in-law, or a scolding sister-in-law. This woman is an old servant of the family and all the business of the house, inside and outside, is in her hands. She has been plundering the family, and brought it to the verge of ruin. The debts now amount to such a sum that no means of paying them off are visible. There is no kind of management. I took it upon myself for a few days to look into some of the ordinary items of housekeeping;

peculation and fraud were discovered at every turn. This interference on my part has made the Mámá my enemy, and she has ever since been set upon stirring up some new cause of ill-feeling every day. She has not been successful so far in doing me any real injury. Still, I have the strongest objection to this Mámá's staying on in the house. But, on the other hand, to get rid of her is no easy matter. All the indebtedness to the different shops has been incurred through her agency. If she heard a rumour of her impending dismissal, she would go off and excite a panic among the creditors. And then the debts are neither by bill nor by book. The whole of the traffic is done orally by guesswork. What I want is that the accounts of all these people should be investigated and put into writing, and that in each case installments of a due proportion should be fixed for future payment, and the practice of borrowing henceforth be abolished, and that the Mámá should be dismissed. I take it for granted that you, too, will come home with my honored father for the Ramazán. All I ask is that you should be so kind as to come round by Lahore, and that by some means or other you will induce my good father-in-law to come home with you for a fortnight at the very least. When all of you gentlemen are present, the whole of this business will be settled admirably.

'I write this letter in a state of grievous disquietude. The Mámá recommended that my bracelets should be pawned. My dear mother-in-law has just this moment gone to my dear aunt's house to make arrangements for some money. No more.'

At the same time that Asghari wrote this letter to her brother, she sent a verbal message across to her aunt, saying that she was alone, and asking her aunt to let Tamásha Khánam come and stay with her for a couple of days, since she had heard that Tamásha Khánam was at present on a visit to her mother. Accordingly that same evening Tamásha Khánam duly arrived. As she got out of her doolie she called out: 'Upon my word, Madam Asghari! I did not think anyone could be so unfriendly. I sent a message to ask you for uncle's letter, and you never let me have it!'

'You don't say so?' said Asghari. 'Who came with the message?'

'Well, you can see her yourself,' said Tamásha Khánam. 'She is here; this Mámá Azmat. Say, old woman—that Friday you came to our house—did I tell you, or not?'

Azmat said: 'Yes, Lady; it is true. She did tell me. I forget everything now, worse luck! By the time I reached this place it was driven out of my head by the housework.'

'Yes,' said Asghari in a low voice; 'you only recollect how to plunder and how to sow strife.' Then she said to Tamásha Khánam: 'The letter is here, and there is another new book just come, full of interesting passages; you can take that home with you when you go.'

Asghari related to Tamásha Khánam the whole story of Mámá Azmat's misdeeds in detail. Tamásha Khánam was a girl of a very hot temper. She was on her feet directly, with her shoe in her hand, eager to give the Mámá a beating. Asghari caught her by the arm and made her sit down again, saying: 'Sister, for God's sake! no such violence. Don't be in a hurry yet awhile; everything will be spoilt.'

Tamásha Khánam said: 'You allow yourself to be set at naught with this circumspection of yours. Sister, if I were in your place, by God's oath! I would make this carrion so smooth after shoe-beatings that she would remember it all her life long.'

Asghari said: 'You will see. Please God! in a few days' time God's judgment will fall on this dishonest woman.'

After that Tamásha Khánam asked: 'What is the reason of your mother-in-law going to her sister's house?'

Asghari said: 'She, too, poor thing, all owing to this ill-conditioned Mámá, is driven about in despair from door to door. There is some banker to whom a sum of money is owing. The Mámá came back to-day, and said he was about to file a suit. She has gone to contrive some plan for *his* money.'

Tamásha Khánam asked: 'Who is the banker who is going to sue her?'

Asghari said: 'I don't know his name.'

Tamásha Khánam asked the Mámá: 'Azmat, what banker is it?'

Azmat said: 'Hazári Mal, Lady.'

Tamásha Khánam said: 'What? The Hazári Mal whose shop is in the Jauhari bázár?'

'Yes, Lady—yes,' said Azmat, 'it is that Hazári Mal.'

Tamásha Khánam said: 'Why, he keeps the accounts of my husband's family. My goodness! what nerve has that wretch got to file a suit? I will tell your cousin[1] when I leave this place. You will see how he will settle matters with him.'

Tamásha Khánam remained two days with Asghari. On the third day she took her leave, and as she was starting she said: 'Asghari, dear, I adjure you by my head—when your father-in-law arrives, and all this affair comes on for trial, mind you make them send for me, and then—you just put Azmat under *my* charge.'

In the Khánam bázár Muhammad Kámil's mother was hospitably detained by her sister, who said to her: 'Dear me, sister! it is but once in a way that you have come here. *Now*, you must stay a week at the least.' But one of the servants was sent to the house every day to inquire after Asghari.

Mámá Azmat incontinently achieved a fresh piece of villainy. The Lieutenant-Governor's camp was expected just at this time, and great pressure was being brought to bear by the magistrate in the matter of conservancy. Notifications were stuck up in every street and mohulla calling upon the inhabitants to make their streets and alleys tidy, to have the fronts of their houses whitewashed, and to keep all the drains and sewers clean, with the warning that, should an accumulation of refuse be found anywhere, the premises would be put up to public auction.[2]

A notification of this kind had been stuck up on the gateway of our friends' mohulla among others. Mámá Azmat went by night and tore down this notification from the gate of the mohulla, and furtively stuck it up over the doorway of the house. Then, just before dawn, she ran off to the Khánam bázár to give Muhammad Kámil's mother intimation. The doors of the house had not yet been opened when she cried out to her at the entrance. Muhammad Kámil's mother recognised her voice, and said: 'Ho there! run, someone, and open the door. Whatever makes Azmat come posting here at such an unearthly hour?' When Azmat appeared before her, she asked: 'Mámá, is all well?'

Azmat said: 'Lady, there is a 'ttachment—a natchment—what do they call the thing?—stuck up on the house. It seems Hazári Mal has filed his suit in court.'

[1]Meaning her own husband.
[2]This is a joke at 'non-regulation procedure.'

Muhammad Kámil's mother said to her sister: 'I am going, my dear; good-bye. If I go, I can send for Hazári Mal, and remonstrate with him. God send pity into his heart!'

Her sister said: 'My dear, I am very much ashamed that I have not been able to arrange for the money. But here is this gold chain off my neck; take that with you. If the business can be settled by pawning it, so much the better; but sell it if you must.'

Muhammad Kámil's mother said: 'You are very kind, dear. I will take the chain. But his money has reached a *terrible* amount; one chain will not go far.'

Her sister said: 'Come, my dear; you know *he*[3] promised that he would procure you a loan from another banker. Get into your doolie, with God's name on your lips. He will be back directly, and I will send him after you.'

In due course Muhammad Kámil's mother arrived at her home. As she got down at the entrance she saw the notification posted on the doorway. In a state of dismal depression she went in silently and sat down. When Asghari heard of her mother-in-law's arrival, she came down from the roof and paid her respects. Seeing her mother-in-law in trouble, she asked: 'Mother, dear! your face looks very sad today.'

Her mother-in-law said: 'Yes; the banker has filed his suit. I cannot see *how* to raise the money any way. Amír Begam, too, has disappointed me, and now a notice has been stuck on the house. What will become of me?'

Asghari said: 'Don't let your honor have the least anxiety. If Hazári Mal *has* filed his suit, it is no harm. He has dealings with Tamásha Khánam's husband's people also, and she promised me that she will take him to task. And if he does not give in, some way will be found of raising the money. What is to be gained by fretting over it?'

Her mother-in-law said: 'If Kámil were here, I would send him to Hazári Mal.'

Asghari said: 'Of course, that is as your honor pleases; but in my opinion it is not proper at all to show any fear of the banker, for otherwise he will have greater boldness in the future, and be holding out

---

[3] *i.e.*, her own husband.

the threat of a suit every day. Far the best plan will be to make no sign
from here, but to bring some influence to bear on him from outside, so
that he may abandon the prosecution of his claim.'

Muhammad Kámil's mother said: 'Tamásha Khánam is still only a
girl. What does she know about the law courts and offices? How would
it be if the business went wrong through relying upon her, while the
time for doing anything applied out of our hands?'

Asghari said: 'No doubt Tamásha Khánam is a girl, but I made it all
thoroughly certain, and I have every confidence.'

While they were still talking, Miyán Muslim gave a shout at the
door. Asghari said: 'See, there is Muslim come. He will have brought
some news about the matter for certain.' Then she made a gesture to
Mahmúda, who went into one of the side-rooms.[4] And she called
Muslim inside, and asked him: 'Muslim, what news have you brought?'

Muslim said: 'My sister sent you her salaam, and asks after your
health, and told me to say that she had Hazári Mal sent for, and gave
him a thorough good frightening, and he made a promise there should
be no suit.'

When she heard this, Muhammad Kámil's mother was comforted
to some extent. But Asghari was amazed. How could this be, that
Tamásha Khánam should send such a message, and yet Hazári Mal
have already filed a suit independently of it? And then the circumstance
of the attachment was altogether extraordinary, for she was in the house
all the time, and heard nothing about it. If it had been an attachment
issued by the judge, surely some chuprassie,[5] or office-runner, would
have called out to the inmates and given them notice.

---

[4]Mahmúda and Muslim being contemporaries and approaching marriageable
age, it was not etiquette for them to see each other.

[5]A chuprassie is a man who carries a badge (chaprás) with his employer's name
on it.

CHAPTER

XIII

When Muslim had taken leave, Asghari said to Mahmúda:
'Go quietly, and tear off the paper which is affixed to the
outer door.'
Mahmúda tore the paper off and brought it in. When Asghari
read it, the order was about conservancy; there was not any mention
of a suit in Court. She guessed at once that this, too, was Azmat's
trickery. She did not, however, make this fact known to her mother-
in-law; but she assured her in the most positive manner that there
was no fear whatever of a suit, and that she might remain perfectly
at ease.

Her mother-in-law said: 'As far as the suit is concerned I feel more
easy from what you tell me; but the Shabebarát[1] and the Ramazán are
coming on to worry me. In both of these festivals it is nothing but
spend, spend. From Lahore, even letters have stopped coming. The
anxiety about this makes my very blood dry up.'

Asghari said: 'There are a good many days yet before the Ramazán.
God is called '*the Causer of causes*;' by that time some provision from
the unseen will be made manifest. True, there are only four days left
now before the Shabebarát; but that is not a festival on which any great
expenditure is required.'

Her mother-in-law said: 'In my house, year after year, twenty rupees

[1]Lit., 'The night of immunity (from sin and sorrow),' a festival analogous to
our All Hallows' Eve. It falls in the month preceding the Ramazán. Pronounce
Shubbay burrát, with the accent on the last syllable, and the 'á' sounded as in 'art.'

goes at the Shabebarát. You can ask for yourself; this Azmat who spends the money is present.'

'Her spending,' said Asghari, 'is nothing to be astonished at. But there are some expenses which cannot be avoided, and there are others which can. And there is nothing so urgent about the Shabebarát to involve the expenditure of so much money.'

Her mother-in-law said: 'Sister, the *Fátiha*[2]—for the saints and the prophets, the great men and elders of our race—is of the *first* importance, and then there is the sending about to people's houses—most necessary. Why, it is but a small matter to mention—I must have five rupees, if there are to be fireworks enough to satisfy your husband and Miss Mahmúda. Muhammad Kámil is married, but what of that? God preserve him! his nature is as full of childish fun as ever it was. Until he has got a hundred fire-fountains[3] and twenty bundles of crackers out of me, he will worry my life out; and Mahmúda, too, will make herself ill with crying.'

Asghari said: 'Five seers[4] of sweets will be quite enough for the Fátiha, and as for the sending about, what comes to us can be despatched elsewhere. And I will talk to Mahmúda; she shall not plague you for crackers this time. You shall see, I will manage the business of the Shabebarát all right somehow. Leave it to me, and do not worry about borrowing money on that account.'

These were her words to her mother-in-law, but Asghari herself was in some trepidation as to how she could keep her husband away from his fire-fountains and crackers. At last she hit on the following plan for conveying her wishes to him so cleverly that she managed to say all she wanted, and yet he was not in the least annoyed.

In Muhammad Kámil's presence she herself broached the subject

---

[2]Fátiha is the name of the opening chapter (seven short verses) of the Qur-án, but the expression here means food consecrated by the recitation of the Fátiha over it, and then distributed.

[3]Called ánár; lit., pomegranates. They are cups of earthenware about the size of a pomegranate, filled with powder and steel filings. There is a very small aperture at the top, and when the cup is set on the ground and lighted the effect is that of a fountain of fire.

[4]A 'seer' is about two pounds.

to Mahmúda by asking: 'Well, sister, what are *your* plans for the Shabebarát?'

Mahmúda replied: 'When my brother brings home his fireworks, he will give some to me, too.'

Before Muhammad Kámil could put in a word, Asghari said: 'You don't suppose your brother will bring you such silly things? What pleasure is there in fireworks, Mahmúda?'

Mahmúda said: 'Sister dear! is it not splendid when they go off?'

'Well,' Asghari said, 'there will be hundreds of them let off in the mohulla; you will be able to watch them from the roof.'

'What!' said Mahmúda; 'and we not let off any?'

'Are you not afraid?' said Asghari.

Mahmúda said: '*I?* I don't let them off with my own hands.'

'Very well,' said Asghari; 'just as you look on when your own are let off, so you may look on when those of the mohulla are let off. And listen, Mahmúda; it is a very bad sport. There is the danger of being burnt. Once, in my mohulla, a fire-fountain burst in a boy's hand; his eyes were blown up, and left quite blank in their sockets. If you want to look on, you should do so at a distance. And, Mahmúda, do you notice your mother's condition? Is she sad, or happy?'

Mahmúda said: 'She is sad, I know.'

Asghari asked: 'Have you ever considered why she is sad?'

Mahmúda said: 'I know nothing about that.'

'Oh!' exclaimed Asghari; 'and yet you say that you are very fond of your mother!'

Mahmúda asked: 'Please, dear sister, why is dear mamma sad?'

Asghari said: 'There's a difficulty about money for the house; the banker won't advance any. She is thinking: "If Mahmúda insists upon having fireworks, where am I to get the money from to give them to her?"'

Mahmúda said: '*I* won't ask for fireworks.'

'Well done!' said Asghari—'well done! You are a very dear sister.'

And she took Mahmúda to her breast and caressed her.

Muhammad Kámil, who was sitting close by, listened to all this without saying a word. Since it was quite reasonable, his heart admitted the force of it, and he immediately went downstairs, and approached his mother, and said: 'Mother, I have heard that you are troubling yourself about the Shabebarát, and I came to ask you not to worry about me. *I don't want any fireworks, and Mahmúda, too, says she will not ask you for any.'*

In this way one item of the expenditure was reduced.

As for the Fátiha, a fine assortment of confectionery was produced at a cost of two rupees. The sending about Asghari took under her own control. When a portion came to the house she did not allow it to be put by. As soon as the man who brought it had gone away she said: 'Take this portion to such and such a place.'

To one after another of all the persons on her list entitled to receive a portion a portion was duly sent. The Shabebarát was kept well for an outlay of two rupees.

Azmat was consumed with rage at this arrangement, and no wonder, since a great item of her perquisites was abolished. Whatever used to come from outside she used to take, and of what was sent from the house she used to purloin half, and for months afterwords she would munch the dried-up sweetmeats that she kept from the Shabebarát instead of a cordial.

CHAPTER

XIV

When the Shabebarát was over, the time drew near for the arrival of Asghari's father, and the next few days passed in no time. Four days before the Ramazán Dúrandesh Khán sáhib arrived in Delhi.

Asghari had taken care to mention her father's coming beforehand, and had settled with her mother-in-law and husband that on whatever day the Tahsildár should arrive she should go home to see him. As soon as she received intimation of his arrival, she at once ordered a doolie, and was set down at her father's house. Her father clasped her to his breast, and was moved to tears; for a long time he kept on asking about her, and giving her an account of himself, and then he said: 'Khairandesh Khán has gone to Lahore in accordance with your honor's order, and, please God, will arrive here tomorrow or next day with your father-in-law.[1] A letter from him reached me on the road. Your father-in-law has obtained his leave.'

So that whole night and all the next day Asghari remained at her mother's house. Shortly before the evening she said to her father: 'If your honor will accord me permission I will now go away.'

Her father said: 'Eh, my dear, you must stay a week. I will send a message to your mother-in-law.'

Asghari said: 'I will do whatever your honor determines, but I think

[1] Lit., with *my* 'co-partner in fathership'. The English language has no term for the connexion between the parents of a bride and of a bridegroom.

it will be the correct thing for me to be in the house before my father-in-law arrives.'

Her father reflected for a bit, and said: 'Yes, that is quite right.'

Accordingly Asghari took leave of her father, and was at home again before sunset. Next day, exactly at the dinner-hour, Muhammad Kámil's father, Maulavi Muhammad Fázil, suddenly appeared on the scene.

I must mention here that the Maulavi[2] sáhib was estate agent to the chief of Lahore. He had a fixed salary of fifty rupees a month from the estate, and the chief was responsible for his house and travelling expenses. Khairandesh Khán had gone to Lahore in accordance with Asghari's written request, and had shown her letter to the Maulavi. When the Maulavi read it he was overjoyed, and though in the ordinary course of things he would probably not have taken leave, yet now in his eagerness to see his daughter-in-law he exerted himself to persuade the chief so as to get a month's leave, and he accompanied Khairandesh Khán on his journey home.

Since Asghari had not yet appeared before her father-in-law after her marriage, when she saw him arrive she went up on to the roof, and stayed there out of bashfulness. Muhammad Kámil's mother was in a state of bewilderment, not understanding why her husband had come. When the meal was over they began to talk. The Maulavi said to his wife: 'Listen to me, madam! your younger daughter-in-law has dragged me hither.' And then he informed her of Asghari's letter, and of Khairandesh Khán's coming, and then he said: 'Fetch the daughter-in-law.'

The mother-in-law went on to the roof, and said: 'Come, daughter, you need not be bashful; why, you used to play in his lap.'

Asghari got up at her mother-in-law's bidding, and went with her, and having made a most respectful obeisance to her father-in-law, sat down.

The Maulavi said: 'Listen, my brother![3] I came here only because you sent for me, and when I saw your letter my soul rejoiced within me. God send His blessing on your youth and grace! In very truth it

[2]This word, pronounced Mowlavee, is equivalent to our *Doctor* (of Divinity or Law).

[3]The use of this term shows that he wished to put her on an equality with himself.

was a happy day for us when you entered our house. Now I feel sure that better days are in store for it, and tomorrow, please God, we will arrange matters in accordance with your wishes and your judgement.'

For two or three days, however, the Maulavi—as was only natural in a man just returned to his home—was occupied in seeing his friends, and after that, for the first few days of the fast, he did not feel disposed to attend to house affairs on account of his fasting. But one day he sent for his daughter-in-law, and made her sit beside him, and then called to Mámá Azmat, and said: 'Mámá, while I am here you must make out all your accounts. Let me take down in writing all the debts which are due to or from anyone. Then I can pay to each of them what may be fitting, and if there is anything left over, I can arrange for paying that by instalments.'

The Mámá said: 'If it were *one* man's bill, perhaps I might keep it in my head to tell you straight off. But the banya, the cloth-merchant, the butcher, the greengrocer, the confectioner—there is money owing to all. And Hazári Mal's account is separate. Whatever your honor may be willing to give to any of them let me have it, and I will go and give it to them; the money shall be placed to your honor's credit in their books.'

The Maulavi sáhib was a good, simple-minded creature. He was on the point of paying the money over to her. Asghari said: 'What is the use of paying sums *on account* in this fashion? First of all find out what is really owing to each, and then pay each one of them after due consideration.'

The Mámá said: 'When I get leisure after dinner I will go round and ask them.'

'What will be the good of your going to *ask?* said Asghari. 'Let each man who is to be paid come here and give in his account.'

The Mámá answered: 'Lady, you have said what is easy to *say*. How am I to go wandering about calling people here at this time? And do you suppose they are likely to leave all their business in order to come with me?'

Asghari said: 'It is not a question of sending for them every day, Mámá. It is only for one day. Go and ask them to come. Some arrangement shall be made for the evening meal; you do no other work today but this. And as for the creditors, they will run when they hear of payment. Hazári Mal went to the Court—a distance of four miles; are his feet swathed in henna bands[4] for coming here? And what distance is it? The greengrocer, the butcher, the banya, and the confectioner all live in this lane. It is only the cloth-seller and Hazári Mal who are at any distance. Keep them over for tomorrow, and let the odds and ends of the accounts be settled today.'

It was not Azmat's wish by any means that the accounts should be gone through at all, but Asghari so overwhelmed her with arguments that she had not a word to offer in reply. First of all the confectioner came. It was asked: 'Well, Lálá, what have you to receive?' The confectioner said: 'Thirty rupees.'

It was asked: 'What things came from your shop? The thirty rupees you talk of is a great deal too much.' The confectioner said: 'Sir, is thirty rupees such a large sum? Why, fifteen rupees' worth of things was had this very Shabebarát. There is one item alone of ten seers of sugar.'

Muhammad Kámil's mother exclaimed: 'Oh you! what sugar? All that was used in the house *this* time for confectionery was bought for ready money in the bázár.'

When Mámá Azmat heard this she grew quite pale; she said to the confectioner: 'What made you enter those ten seers of sugar to *their* account? I took that for another family, and, moreover, I told you as much.'

The confectioner said: 'You never mentioned anyone else's name to me. You took it for this gentleman's house. What good should I get from entering another person's things to his name? Besides, I have not an account with any other gentleman's family.'

The Mámá was reduced to mere incoherent expressions of her anger. The Maulavi sáhib said: 'Well, let the item of the sugar stand over. Tell us the other things.'

Accordingly the man named in the same way a whole number of other things which had never entered the house in its lifetime. Four

---

[4]Henna is applied to the feet (of women and children) by means of bandages (something like a poultice) kept on during the night.

seers of *bálushahí*[5] for the 'Illustrious Birth', and the best of it was that in this family no one had ever held a birthday assemblage.[6] In the end some six or seven rupees alone were found to be correct, and the rest all false.

The Maulavi sáhib's soul took fire at this, and his wrath knew no bounds. He cried out: 'How now, you rascally Azmat, have you contrived to put the debts of the whole world upon this family? Have you levelled this house with the dust simply for fun?'

When the confectioner was done with the greengrocer came. He said: 'Master, my account is a standing one—two annas' worth of vegetables a day.'

Muhammad Kámil's mother exclaimed: 'What's that? Only one seer of vegetables comes to this house. Is that two annas a day?'

The greengrocer said: 'Your highness, the Mámá takes three seers from the shop.'

The Mámá said: 'Yes. I take three seers—one seer for you, one seer for my daughter, and one seer for another family. Do I deny it? This wretch charges the whole of it to you.'

The greengrocer said: 'Eh, you wicked, dishonest old woman! you have been taking that amount for years against the account of this family, and whenever I have got my money it has been from this family that I got it.'

When the butcher's and banya's accounts were gone into a thousand frauds were discovered in them also, and it was proved that the Mámá had been helping to keep her own daughter Khairátan, and the families of two or three neighbours out of the purchases for this one family; nay, she would have a purchase debited against the house, and then sell it elsewhere. But to proceed—all the petty miscellaneous accounts were finished by the evening; there now only remained those of the cloth-merchant and Hazári Mal. The Maulavi sáhib said: 'Have done with it now for today; we will see to the rest tomorrow.' But he added in a low voice: 'It won't do for Azmat to run off.'

[5]A kind of sweetmeat, so called from its powdery surface, bálu meaning sand.
[6]A gathering, partly social and partly religious, at which certain texts and prayers are recited in commemoration of the birth of the Prophet.

Asghari said: 'It is hardly likely she will run away now and leave her family and all her belongings, and her house and children. True, if she has any sense of shame she may eat or drink something,[7] but if she were of that sort how should she act in such a manner? Certainly she ought to be looked after, but only so far that someone should keep a watch over her when she is going backwards and forwards.'

Orders were then given privately to one of the servants who had come with the Maulavi to keep an eye upon the Mámá's movements.

[7] *i.e.*, take poison.

CHAPTER
XV

❧❧

When the dinner was well over the Mámá got up stealthily and went outside. The servant followed behind. First of all the Mámá went to her own house, and from thence, having thrust something under her arm, she went as straight as an arrow to the house of the cloth-merchant, and hailed him. The cloth-merchant came out astonished, and said: '*You* here at this time, old lady!'

Azmat said: 'The Maulavi sáhib has come home. The accounts of everyone whom he has to pay are being gone through. Tomorrow you too will be summoned, and then—don't you say anything that may bring about my disgrace.'

The cloth-merchant said: 'What is there in the accounts that should cause disgrace to you?'

The Mámá replied: 'Lála! can't you understand? This wretched covetousness is a bad, bad thing. In the master's name I have taken for myself too, now and again, from your shop a piece of long cloth, or muslin, or English stuff.'

The cloth-merchant said: 'How am I to know what things you have taken on your own account?'

The Mámá said: 'I have not my wits about me at this moment to reckon it up, but four pieces of English stuff, and some rolls of muslin, and ten yards of red calico will be the outcome of what is mine. Here, take these four bangles—off my own wrists—they are sixteen rupees' worth—perhaps one rupee less now for wear—knock off fifteen rupees from the total against *their* name, and if there *should* be a few more rupees found due from me I am prepared to pay them.'

The cloth-merchant said: 'Well, I will take the bangles, as you give them to me. But it is night now; my books are at the shop; without looking at them how can I tell what is gone, and how much is due to me?'

Azmat said: 'This time my honor is in your hands. Screen me however you can.'

After leaving the cloth-merchant she went straight to the house of Hazári Mal. He too was amazed, and said: 'What! *you* here at this time of night!'

She fell at his feet, and, bursting into tears, began saying, 'I have done something wrong.'

Hazári Mal said: 'What is that?'

'Oh, promise me,' said Azmat, 'that you will forgive me, and then I will tell you.'

Hazári Mal said: 'Say what it is, can't you?'

Azmat said: 'Four months ago some money for the house came from Lahore, and the Maulavi sáhib sent one hundred rupees for you. All of that money I spent, and out of sheer fright I never made it known to the master's family. Now the Maulavi sáhib has come, and he will send for you to reckon up with him. I will make some arrangement to secure those rupees, but I want you not to let the amount be known.'

Hazári Mal said: 'If it were a matter of two or three rupees I could keep it dark, but a lump sum of a hundred rupees could not be hushed up whatever I did.'

The Mámá said: 'What, is not my credit good even for a hundred rupees?'

Hazári Mal said: 'The plain truth is that your credit is not even good for a cowrie. When you have behaved in this manner to a family whose bread you have eaten all your life, is it likely you should prove an honest client to anyone else?'

'Ah, Lálá,' said Azmat, 'when bad luck befalls a woman her friends become her enemies. Well, then, if you will not trust me—here, take these bracelets and armlet of my daughters in deposit.'

Hazári Mal said: 'Yes, that is talking business. Only, if it were daylight the things could be assayed, and then we should know what they are worth. But, at a guess, the whole lot will be worth from fifty to sixty rupees.'

Azmat said: 'Oh, oh, Lálá, don't be so cruel! it is just four months since I had the things made. They cost me a hundred or a hundred and twenty-five rupees.'

Hazári Mal said: 'What is there to fret about? *Your* property—it may be worth a hundred, it may be worth two hundred—no one is robbing you of it. But when I have got it weighed, it will be known exactly what the value of it is.'

When she had made all these arrangements the Mámá returned to her house, and the Maulavi sáhib's servant recounted all the circumstances to him, as he was shampooing his feet.[1] Asghari, too, was made acquainted with all the facts by Muhammad Kámil's mother.

The next morning Hazári Mal and the cloth-merchant were sent for. As the accounts proceeded objections began to be raised. The Mámá's voice grew louder and louder in the discussion. The cloth-merchant said: 'Old woman, what are *you* making such a noise about! Here, pick up those bangles of yours;[2] you declared they were worth fifteen rupees; they value them at nine in the bázár.'

Upon this Hazári Mal produced the bracelets, and armlet, and laid them down before the company, and said to Azmat: 'Excuse me, madam, these valuables are of no good to me.'

The Maulavi sáhib inquired of the two men: 'How, brothers! what is the meaning of these things?'

Then both of them rehearsed the story of the previous night, and Azmat's face was as though it were slapped by a hundred thousand shoes.

When all the accounts were finally settled, and the Maulavi sáhib had brought out the money for payment, he distributed to each person one-half of the sum to which he was justly entitled, and said: 'I have sent to Lahore for some more money, which will arrive in a few days, and then the remainder shall be paid in full.'

[1] To induce sleep.
[2] This implies that he had thrown down in front of her.

All the men asked: 'And what has been found due to us from the Mámá—from whom are we to get that?'

It was during this conversation that Muslim passed by the house on his way from school, and heard what was going on. As soon as he got home, he said to Tamásha Khánam: 'There is a huge crowd collected to-day at the entrance to sister Asghari's house. Her father-in-law is making up the accounts.'

Directly she heard this, Tamásha Khánam got into her doolie, and went to the spot. As soon as she was set down, she began scolding Asghari, and said: 'How now, madam! you never let me know after all? What has happened?'

Asghari said: 'The accounts are still being settled. If all that bother had been over, I would have let you know.'

To make a long story short, the Maulavi sáhib told all the people that what was due to them from the Mámá they must get out of the Mámá; and then he turned to the Mámá, and said: 'Your highness! pay these people their money.'

Azmat kept her eyes on the ground, and said: 'My daughter's ornaments are with me. Let them divide between them what they can make out of those.'

All her daughter's ornaments, however, went in liquidating one-half only of the claims of the greengrocer, the butcher, the banya, and the cloth-merchant. For Hazári Mal's hundred rupees she was obliged to mortgage the hut she lived in. A deed was written out on stamped paper then and there, and four respectable citizens attested it.

Then the Maulavi sáhib said to Azmat: 'Your honor will now be pleased to take your departure in peace. For a disloyal, treacherous, deceitful woman like you there is no room in my house.'

Asghari said: 'She possesses one other quality besides disloyalty; shall I tell you what that is? She spent her time in devising schemes for sowing mischief in the household. Eh, Azmat, do you remember about the *karhá-i* which Mahmúda's brother expressed a wish for, and you went and delivered a lying message from me that "the bride says she has a headache?" Speak out now, and tell us *when* did you mention any wish of his to me, and *when* did I make the excuse of a headache?'

Azmat said: 'Lady, you were reading the Qur-án on the roof. I went up to tell you, but when I saw you reading, I came back again.'

'And the story of the headache,' said Asghari, 'was your own invention?'

Azmat said: 'What I thought was this—you had been reading the Qur-án from the early morning to that time; was it likely you would bother your head about cooking?'

Asghari said: 'Well, then, how do you explain your saying that I was going to the hills? Did I ever take *you* into my confidence? Did you ever hear me *speak* of such a thing?'

To this question Azmat could make no reply. Then Asghari produced the notification, and threw it down in front of the Maulavi sáhib, saying: 'Just look at that; my lady Azmat here is capable of *this kind* of thing. She herself tore off the notification from the gate of the Mohulla, and she herself posted it up on this house; and then she herself went running all the way to my dear mother to tell her about it.'

While Asghari went on recounting these facts the Maulavi sáhib's countenance grew redder and redder. On the other side of the room Tamásha Khánam was grinding her teeth. The Maulavi said: 'It is not enough to turn you out. You are a thoroughly wicked woman.' And having said this, he shouted to his servant, and said: 'Bahádur! take this unclean creature to the police-station, and, stay—I will write all her story in a note at once.'

But Asghari said to the Maulavi sáhib: 'It is enough; she has reached her own punishment. Spare her from the police.' And she made a sign to Azmat to take herself off. Indeed she went with her as far as the outer door.

So after all her pranks was Mámá Azmat turned out of this house. When she got home her daughter fell upon her like a fury, crying out: 'Did I not say to you: "Don't, mother, don't go in for robbing on this scale. If a hundred days last for the thief, one day is sure to come for the merchant; take care lest one day you be caught"? Whose words did you care for? The right thing has happened. As you did so you have received. But don't make *my* name evil now in my husband's home. Go away wherever your God may lead you. There is no work for you in my house. As for the jewels, I have submitted to Providence; if it be written in my fate they will come to me again.'

CHAPTER

XVI

In this manner, after many prayers, Asghari succeeded in routing her enemy, and freed the whole family from an incubus. When Azmat's case had been decided, Asghari asked permission a second time to go to her father, which being gladly accorded, she took leave, and arrived at her mother's house. There she stayed for a whole week: and everything in which she desired her father's advice was discussed by her in full. Her father asked, 'Has Azmat been got rid of?'

Asghari said: 'By your honor's gracious favour everything has turned out well. If my elder brother had not gone to Lahore my father-in-law would never have come, nor would this account of years have been settled, nor would Azmat have been dismissed.'

The Khán sáhib asked: And how will the management of the house go on now?'

Asghari said: 'As soon as the Mámá was ousted I came here. But there will not be any difficulty now in the management. It was only Azmat who caused the trouble. *Now* I will look after everything myself.'

The Khán sáhib asked: 'What other plans have you started there?'

Asghari said: 'As yet I have not given my attention to anything. From the very beginning I was encountered with the difficulty about Azmat. I hope now to look into every matter and set things in order; and, please God, I will keep your honor informed of whatever happens by letter.'

The Khán sáhib had made Asghari a monthly allowance after her marriage of ten rupees. He now inquired whether he should give her any money before his departure in case she should be in difficulty about the household expenses. Asghari replied: 'Those ten rupees are really more than I require; in fact, up to date I have them all in hand, and if I took more, what should I do with them? If any need should arise I will ask your honor myself.'

After this Asghari took leave of her father, and came back. When she arrived at her mother-in-law's house she found her mother-in-law busy blowing up the kitchen fire, and asked in amazement: 'Dear, dear! has not a new Mámá been engaged yet?'

Her mother-in-law said: 'As far as that goes several women have *come* for the place, but when I heard the wages they asked I had not the courage to engage any of them. Azmat was a bad woman, but she served us for twenty-five years at eight annas[1] a month. Now, whatever Mámá comes here, I find she will not take less than two rupees and her food. I put it off till you should come back.'

Asghari said: 'There is a Mámá whom *I* have in my eye, but she too asks high wages—Kifáyat Nisá's younger sister, Diyánat Nisá.[2] She can cook, and do needlework, and all that; and Kifáyat Nisá once told me that she was ready to go into service if she could find a good situation.'

Muhammad Kámil's mother asked: 'What wages will she take?'

Asghari replied: 'She *said* she wanted three rupees a month and her food. But with a little talking over she will probably be content with two.'

'If we are to give two rupees a month and food,' said Muhammad Kámil's mother, 'there is Chuniya's mother (I mean Chuniya the daughter of Bhondu the sutler) begging for the place, and she lives across the way.'

Asghari said: 'I would not take Chuniya's mother even at four annas a month.'

Muhammad Kámil's mother said: 'Eh, why not?'

Asghari said: 'It is not good to have a woman living close by. Your eyes are off her for a minute, and she can pick up whatever she fancies,

[1]In those days equal to one shilling, but now about eight pence.
[2]Diyánat means 'Probity'.

and take it home and be back again in no time. And with the houses so near to each other Chuniya's mother will be always going home, and will very likely stay there all night.'

Muhammad Kámil's mother said: 'Bakhshu's wife has often spoken to me on behalf of her daughter Zulfan, and Zulfan lives in Saiyid Firúz's cottages.'

Asghari asked: 'Is it that Zulfan who always dresses so finely?'

Muhammad Kámil's mother said: 'Yes; does she dress so very finely? She is lately married; she has rather a taste for good clothing.'

Asghari said: '*That* kind of person is not the sort to engage.'

Muhammad Kámil's mother said: 'Zulfan's mother is willing to take service herself.'

Asghari said: 'She has a kite's tail sticking to her always in the shape of her little daughter, who does not leave hold of her mother for a minute. In that way we shall be said to have one servant, but at meals there will be two.'

Muhammad Kámil's mother said: 'There is not anyone else that I can think of.'

'Look here,' said Asghari, 'I will send for that Diyánat Nisá.'

'And what about the wages?' said Muhammad Kámil's mother.

Asghari said: 'To get an honest servant for small wages is impossible. It would suit us to give three instead of two rupees to people of this kind; but I do not fancy giving a woman like Azmat even eight annas a month to let the house be robbed by her. That saying is true enough: "Dear for a good reason, cheap for a bad cause".'

The meal for that day was cooked by the mother-in-law and daughter-in-law together. When it was over Asghari took Mahmúda with her, and went up on to the roof. As long as the Maulavi sáhib was in the house Asghari curtailed her habit of coming down from the roof considerably; moreover, she impressed it upon Mahmúda that she was not to be always running downstairs. Mahmúda was but a little girl; she asked her sister-in-law: 'Dearest, why not?'

Asghari replied: 'People do not go running about as they like in the presence of their elders.'

After dinner there began to be a quarrel between the Maulavi sáhib and his wife over the accounts of the housekeeping. His wife complained that he sent her far too small a sum for expenses; that upon *her*, living at home, fell all the arrangements for weddings, the obligations to the family connections, journeys to and fro, keeping up the feasts, and what not. The Maulavi sáhib declared that twenty rupees a month was not too small a sum, that his wife had not the gift of good management, and that was the reason why such an unhappy state of things prevailed in the house. In the middle of it all the Maulavi shouted out for Mahmúda, and when she came, he said: 'Call your sister-in-law here.'

When Asghari heard of her being summoned, she was amazed, and thought to herself: 'Why do they send for me now?' She asked Mahmúda: 'What is going on?'

Mahmúda said: 'There is a quarrel going on.'

When Asghari went in the Maulavi sáhib said: '*You* tell me, sonnie, who will do the housekeeping now?'

Asghari said: 'My dear mother will do it just as she always has done.'

The Maulavi sáhib said: 'I have seen what comes of *her* doing it. Fancy a house getting twenty rupees a month, and a state like this! not a single cooking-pot fit to use, and nothing respectable. If one wants a teaspoonful of sherbet at any time, God willing, you won't find the means of getting it in this house.'

Asghari said: 'What fault of the mother's is there in that? That wretched Azmat ruined the house.'

The Maulavi sáhib said: 'Azmat would have had no power if *she* had had the sense to govern it. Azmat was a servant, not the mistress of the family.'

Asghari said: 'When a woman of her age, and of twenty-five years' service in a house, girds up her loins to rob it, who can discover her frauds? One cannot suspect an old servant of that kind.'

'But after all,' said the Maulavi sáhib, 'you *did* suspect her, did you not?'

Asghari said: '*I* suspect her? It was her evil genius which prompted her when she started that story about the lawsuit, and so stirred up a nest of sleeping hornets.'

Here the mother-in-law intervened: 'Out of fifty rupees you keep thirty for your own single self, and here, for the whole family, only twenty!'

The Maulavi sáhib said: 'There is no comparison between the expenses of living at home and abroad! You have counted me as a single person; what about the servants, the travelling equipment, the house, the clothes?'

His wife said: 'You get your travelling expenses and house from the chief.'

The Maulavi sáhib said: 'I get a *horse*, but I have to supply the corn and grass for feeding it out of my own purse; the groom is four rupees a month. And the house has to be kept in repair. Then I have to keep up a position befitting the chief's court, and money going and coming— a thousand worries. It is a wonder to me how I get on at all.'

Asghari addressed her mother-in-law, and said: 'Mother dear, what is the use of quarrelling about the twenty rupees? A thousand thanks for what we do get. If God will send a blessing upon the dear father's earnings, that is worth thousands.'

Her mother-in-law said: 'Daughter, the house cannot be kept going on twenty rupees by *me*.'

Asghari restrained her mother-in-law by a look, and said to the Maulavi sáhib: 'Your honor, if it please you, give two rupees *less* even than you have been giving; but whatever you are pleased to give, let it arrive punctually month by month. When at the right moment there is not a farthing forthcoming, one is obliged to borrow, and through borrowing whatever vestige of good luck remains to a family is blown away.'

The Maulavi sáhib said: 'The rules for payment of salaries in these Hindustani Courts are very bad. Sometimes they are distributed after six months, sometimes you only get them after a whole year. That is the reason why one cannot regulate one's expenses. But before I go, I will tell Hazári Mal to give you twenty rupees every month regularly.'

Asghari inquired: 'Suppose the banker debits your honor for the advances, will he not require interest?'

The Maulavi sáhib said: 'No, he will not take interest. He has a standing account with the chief's estate; an order shall be sent from there.'

Asghari said: 'Then that will be all right.'

Accordingly twenty rupees was fixed as the monthly allowance.

But Muhammad Kámil's mother did not like the arrangement, and when they were alone together she complained to Asghari.

Asghari said: 'Please God! I will manage the house upon twenty. Don't let your honor be alarmed about it. And, as a matter of fact, the Maulavi sáhib cannot keep up his position properly upon less than thirty rupees. In the profession of agent in the first place, there is no chance of any extraneous receipts[3] and if there were, you would not expect the Maulavi sáhib to take them, would you? Thus it is a case of "the slices counted, the soup measured". Suppose two or three rupees more did come for the house, and the Maulavi sáhib should live in discomfort himself, that would not be right.'

Her mother-in-law listened to this, and made no more ado. Asghari sent for Diyánat Nisá, and after some conversation, got her to agree to two rupees a month and her food; and she cautioned her in these words: 'Mind that you are careful, Diyánat Nisá, and do not let anything happen which might force us to alter our good opinion of you. As your elder sister conducts herself in *my* home, so do you here.'

Diyánat Nisá said: 'Lady, may God send my death to me in that hour when I cast an eye upon what is not my own property! If need be I will ask you, and then eat; but to taste even a pinch of salt without your order I hold abominable.'

[3] An euphemism for 'bribes'.

CHAPTER
XVII

❧

On the day after the Eed, the Maulavi sáhib started on his
journey to Lahore. Asghari at once laid in a stock of all the
things that were necessary, and henceforth she continued
regularly to lay in stocks of things at their proper season whenever she
found they were cheap. Chillies, onions, coriander-seed, grain, different
kinds of pulse, rice, sugar, firewood and other fuel, potatoes, yams,
turnips, fenugreek, fennel-leaves, and what not, were all purchased in
turn at the proper time. Including the Mámá, the household consisted
of five persons. Twice a day a pound and a half of meat arrived, out of
which Diyánat managed always to provide two varieties of fare.
Sometimes she cooked half with vegetables, and half plain; sometimes
she made one half into *kabábs*; and once a day *dál*, and every seventh
day *pulá-o*, and sweetened rice were standing dishes. Two or three kinds
of chutney—some sweet, some flavoured with essence of mint, and some
with vinegar—and several kinds of preserves, were made by Asghari at
home and stored. And in addition to these she provided one bottle each
of sherbet of pomegranate, syrup of lime-juice, sherbet of violets, sherbet
of lilies, and sherbet of fálsa.[1] A supply of everything that was requisite
was regularly kept up, and notwithstanding this abundance the expenditure in each month did not exceed fifteen rupees. Out of the five rupees
which were left over there were gradually purchased two large platters,

[1]The fálsa is a shrub bearing a small purple berry, much esteemed for making
cooling drinks. The botanical name is *Grewia Asiatica*.

weighing five and ten seers, a tray, some small spoons, two drinking-vessels, one complete tea-set, and so on. Also she had two boxes made, and two chests of drawers—one for the kitchen, and one for the store-closet—and two new beds were furnished. In a word, out of her twenty rupees, Asghari furbished up the house to such an extent that in outward appearance it assumed a look of considerable grandeur. Thrift and good order were introduced by her into everything.

In Azmat's time, three or four pice worth of goodies were fetched from the bázár every day for Mahmúda's sake, since there was never a crumb left over from the family meals. Now, at both meals three or four chupatties began to remain on the tablecloth, and for Mahmúda she would sometimes set by a couple of bits of egg apple, or she would let her have a pinch of coarse sugar, or she would give her a slice of preserved fruit. The daily sending to the bázár for sweets was stopped. Occasionally, for a treat, if Mahmúda had set her heart on anything, it was sent for.

For a whole lifetime no poor man had ever received from the family so much as a handful of meal, or half a chupattie. Now, after each of the two daily meals, two chupatties were given away to the poor. Whatever things there were in the house used formerly to be left lying about in wonderful misarrangement, like cabbage-leaves or radishes. Now everything was in the right place. If you ask for the bundles of clothes, they are all tied up and arranged in order, with the clothes neatly folded inside them. Every vessel in the closet where the grain is stored, and water kept, is carefully covered up.[2] The dishes, clean and bright, are put away in their proper places; those of china and those of copper apart. It was as if the house were a machine, with all its works in good order, and the key of the machine in Asghari's hands. Whenever she turned it, the machine began moving of itself.

As time went on, two rupees or four rupees began to be saved every month, and Asghari credited them to a separate account as a deposit on trust. The practice of borrowing had been forsworn from the day when Asghari took the management of the house into her own hands. Not even by chance was a farthing's worth of goods ever got from the

---

[2]The grain (including pulse) and also the water are stored in large earthen-ware jars placed in a row.

bázár on credit. Asghari used to write down all the accounts of the house in a book. When anything came to be nearly used up, and Diyánat Nisá reported, 'Lady, there is only enough ghee for two days more,' Asghari got out her book, and looked in it to see on what date what amount of ghee was purchased, and how much the daily consumption was. If the calculation did not tally she subjected Diyánat Nisá to a cross-examination. It was not possible that any wasteful expenditure should occur, or things be made away without being accounted for. Even the reckonings of the corn-grinder[3] and the washerwoman were duly entered in Asghari's book.

[3]The corn is purchased whole and ground in the house under strict supervision by women called in for the purpose.

As soon as everything was in working order, and some method had been established in the house, Asghari turned her attention to other matters. Muhammad Kámil was *studying*, but in the desultory and half-hearted manner in which boys who are left to their own resources and their own devices are apt to study. His father, as we have seen, lived away from home; Muhammad Aqil, though he *was* the elder brother—still, the difference between the two was not more than two and a half years—at any rate, he did not exercise any control over him. Muhammad Kámil did his lessons morning and evening, but he also used to play with the boys of his own age at cards, or chess, or draughts. On several occasions, when he was engaged in some game, he would not come home till three full hours of the night had gone. Asghari knew all about this, but she was seeking for some opportunity that would enable her to speak abut it in such a way as not to give offence.

One day, Muhammad Kámil came home very late at night, and (possibly he had been winning before he came) he was in good spirits. Directly he came in he asked for supper. Diyánat Nisá ran to warm up the sauce. Muhammad Kámil thought it was just being cooked, and asked: 'Mámá, is not your pot off the fire yet?'

Asghari said: 'It has been taken off and put on again several times already. You eat your meals at such unreasonable hours that the supper gets cold, and is perfectly ruined. Either make some arrangement to take your meals in good time, or else get your supper outside. At present your dear mother is put to inconvenience every day with our waiting for you.'

Muhammad Kámil said: 'Eh, do you people wait for me? I thought for certain you would have your own meals.'

Asghari said: 'When there are men in the house, what need is there for women to be gobbling up their meals?'

Muhammad Kámil said: 'That might do if it were a matter of a few days. But what is the use of insisting on it? Eat your own suppers in future.'

Asghari kept silence for the time. When they were on the roof, Muhammad Kámil himself began talking on the subject in the same way. Asghari said to him: 'It is an extraordinary thing that you cannot do anything which is contrary to your habits, and yet you wish us to act contrary to ours. Why don't you come home earlier?'

Muhammad Kámil said: 'One does not care to go out again after supper, and sleep does not come to me till late. I get stupid, stopping in the house without any occupation. That is why I come home late, on purpose, so that I may go to bed directly after supper.'

Asghari said: 'Occupation is a matter within one's own power. There are a thousand things to do if a man regulates his time properly. The one occupation of reading takes up plenty of time. I used to see my eldest brother at his books often until midnight, and if by chance he went to sleep he used to make a great lamentation. You do not work hard enough at your reading; that is why you get so bored at the want of occupation.'

Muhammad Kámil said: 'How much harder ought I to work? I do my lessons both times. I learn by heart what is set me.'

Asghari said: 'I don't understand what it is that you do learn. That day when Azmat's accounts were going on, your dear father asked you some question about a sum, and you could not tell him. I felt quite ashamed.'

Muhammad Kámil said: 'Accounts are a different branch of study. I am reading Arabic; that has nothing to do with accounts.'

Asghari said: 'The object of learning things is that one's business with the outer world should never come to a standstill. My eldest brother has read a lot of Arabic and Persian, but he cannot get an appointment.

My father tells him that until he learns how to keep accounts and do office work he need not expect to be employed. Now Ma-álandesh[1] is studying at college, and he knows more about keeping accounts than his elder brother. My father is delighted with him, and says that if he goes on reading at college for another two years, he will get him a place under Government.'

Muhammad Kámil said: 'They only take young fellows at college; I am past the age.'

Asghari said: 'You are not bound to enter the college. Are there not lots of private tutors in the city? Just give as much of your time to this as you now waste in gambling.'

Muhammad Kámil said: 'Why, come now, I am not gambling all day and night. It is only now and then that I sit down to it for an hour or so.'

Asghari said: 'Gambling is a habit like opium eating. It begins with a little, but goes on increasing until at length it becomes a second nature, and there is no getting rid of it. In the first place, these amusements are sinful; but, besides that, they hinder a man from acquiring any other proficiency. Men of worth and merit never gamble; it is the good-for-nothing people who kill their time in this way. However much a man may rejoice at winning in these games, there is every bit as much grief in losing at them; and just as the joy of winning is unreal, so is the grief at losing unreasonable. Often, too, when people go on playing together, gratuitous disputes arise between them. If you will take my advice, you will give up these games entirely. People do not say anything about it in your presence, but behind your back they have their jest. It was only the day before yesterday that a young fellow came in search of you; the Mámá answered from inside that the young gentleman has gone out. The young fellow said to his companion: "Come along to Master[2] Husaini's house, we shall find him there in the crush over the chess." Your dear father's name stands high in the city; people have great faith in him; but going to such places

[1]There is a meaning in all these names. The father's name Dúrandesh may be translated 'far seeing'. The elder brother's Khairandesh means 'looking to the good', and Ma-álandesh may be translated as 'looking to the main chance'.

[2]'Master' here means 'schoolmaster'.

gives a man a bad name; and I have heard your father, too, lamenting over his bad fortune that neither of his two sons has grown up to be such as he would rejoice to see them. He said of Aqil that, though he had been given a good education, he had now forgotten what he learnt in the absorbing pursuit of his office work; but he said of his younger son: '*He* has no leisure from play and sport.' Indeed, some one or other had carried the information to my own dear father; he spoke to me about it; but I said: "It is all a lie. If anything of the kind went on I should be sure to know of it".'

This remonstrance of Asghari's had a very good effect upon Muhammad Kámil. He left off gambling altogether, and began to devote himself to his Arabic with much more zeal than formerly; and he commenced learning to keep accounts, and other things, from one of the schoolmasters out of school hours. God has conferred a special blessing upon *time*. By spending his time according to rule, Muhammad Kámil before many days were over had made considerable progress in Arabic, and he had also read through and mastered several books on mathematics.

CHAPTER
XIX

❧❧

While Muhammad Kámil was employing his energies in this direction, Asghari had the opportunity of starting a new enterprise. In the mohulla in which their house was there resided a personage of very great importance—the Hakím Rúhullah Khán.[1] The Hakím sáhib himself was treasurer to the Mahárája in the state of Patiyála, but his family and children lived in the mohulla. What with the house, and the grounds, and the servants, and dependents, it was a vast establishment; and the family was reckoned as one of the highest rank in the city. They had formed alliances with the best families, and were in the pick of society. The Hakím sáhib's younger brother, Fatihullah Khán, was for a long time manager-in-chief of the estate of the Ruler of Indore, but when Munshi Ammu Ján's power was in the ascendant in that State he thought it best under the circumstances to retire. He possessed, however, lakhs of rupees of his own, and was quite independent of service. He had purchased many thousands of rupees worth of property in the city, and the monthly rents which came in alone amounted to several hundreds. He lived in great state; there was a guard of sepoys at the entrance to his house, and, inside and outside, some thirty or forty servants. Horses, elephants, pálkis, carriages, always ready, in case he should go out.

[1] The title of 'Hukeem', which means 'Physician', may have been hereditary, since there is a great tendency in India to address people by titles earned by their ancestors. Or it may be that each of the brothers had qualified himself to be a physician in order to give advice gratis to the poor, a species of charity which is by no means uncommon among wealthy Musalmans.

Fatihullah Khán had two daughters—Jamálára and Husnára. Jamálára had been married to the son of the Nawáb Isfandiyár Khán, but they got on so badly together that at last all intercourse between them was broken off. Not (God forbid it!) that there was any divorce; but still, there was no longer any pretence of affection. Even the articles of the bride's trousseau[2] had been sent back to her. Husnára had been betrothed into the family of the Nawáb of Jhajjar. The Aunt on the mother's side of these two girls, Sháh Zamáni begam, lived in the mohulla in which Asghari's mother resided, and in that mohulla Asghari's ability was the subject of common talk. Sháh Zamáni, too, knew all about her, and had also seen her upon several occasions at weddings or other functions. Now it happened that Sháh Zamáni begam came to pay her younger sister, Husnára's mother, a visit.

It is in the order of this world that no human being is exempt from sorrow, and doubtless this has been so ordained by Providence, since if any person were happy in all respects he would not remember his God even in his moments of leisure, nor think of himself as only God's servant. Sháh Zamáni's sister Sultána begam had every worldly gratification at her command, yet she was a constant prey to feelings of mortification in regard to her daughters. On the one hand, here was Jamálára, after all the ceremonies of her marriage had been fully completed, sitting neglected at home. On the other hand, Husnára had developed such a trick of ill-temper that she was on bad terms with everyone living in the house. She had no reverence for her mother, nor respect for her elder sister, nor fear of her father. There was not a servant who had not some special complaint against her, not a maid who was not asking to be protected from her. Husnára had raised the whole household against herself.

When Sháh Zamáni arrived one would have supposed that Husnára, conscious of the fact that this was her mother's elder sister, would have sat quiet for half an hour or so. Not a bit of it. Sháh Zamáni had barely time to get out of her pálki, when she was assailed by a series of complaints one after another. Nargis came up with tears in her eyes,

---

[2]These would include not only clothes and jewellery, but all the cooking apparatus and a great deal of the furniture of the bride's apartments.

and said: 'Look, Begam sáhib, the young lady has torn my new dopatta to shreds.' Sosan raised a complaint: 'Begam sáhib, the young lady has left the mark of her teeth on my neck.' Guláb sobbed out: 'My ear is all red with blood.'[3] The nurse screamed: 'Look at *this!* she has hit my poor little girl such a blow with a stick that there is great weal on her arm.' And from the kitchen the Mámá sent up a cry: 'See, she is throwing handfuls and handfuls of ashes into the stewing-pans.'

Sháh Zamáni begam called out to her: 'Husná, come here!'

Recognising her Aunt's voice, Husnára did at last come forward, but without any greeting or obeisance. Her hands covered with ashes, and her feet all muddy—just as she was—she ran and seized hold of her Aunt.

Her Aunt said: 'Husná, you have grown very rude.'

Husnára said: 'This old hag Nargis had been telling tales, I suppose,' and so saying she got away from her Aunt's lap, and ran and pulled Nargis's hair. Her Aunt called out 'Oh! oh!' repeatedly, but she listened to nothing.

Sháh Zamáni turned to her sister, and said: 'Sister Sultána, for Heaven's sake get a governess for this child.'

Sultána begam said: 'My dear sister, what can I do? I have been in search of a governess for months; there is none to be had.'

Sháh Zamáni begam said: 'Oho, sister! is the old proverb true of you also: "With the boy in her lap, *Lost child!* cried all over the city." Why, in your own mohulla there is the young bride just come to Maulavi Muhammad Fázil's house—a governess who is one in a hundred thousand.'

Sultána said: 'I never heard about it till this moment. See, I will send someone at once.' And then she called for the superintendent of the household, and said: 'Máni ji, there is some Maulavi sáhib living in this mohulla; my dear elder sister says that his youngest daughter-in-law is very highly educated. Look you, if she is willing to take service as a governess, go and bring her here. I am prepared to give her food and clothing, and ten rupees a month, with pocket-money for pawn and tobacco; and when the girl shall have finished her first

---

[3]Nargis (Narcissus), Sosan (Lily), and Guláb (Rose), are names of the female attendants.

portion of the Qur-án, and shall have learnt good manners, I will give the governess something to gratify her independently of her salary.'

Máni ji went to the Maulavi sáhib's house. She was received by Muhammad Kámil's mother, and after the usual courtesies, she asked: 'My good madam, are you the Maulavi sáhib's wife?'

Diyánat Nisá replied: 'Yes, this is the lady; come and sit down; where have you come from?'

Máni ji said: 'Where is your younger daughter-in-law?'

Muhammad Kámil's mother replied: 'On the roof.'

Máni ji asked: 'Shall I go up there to her?'

Diyánat Nisá said: 'Your honor will kindly tell us your address and situation. The lady-bride will come here to receive you.'

Máni ji said: 'I am come from the Hakím sáhib's house.'

Muhammad Kámil's mother inquired after the health of each member of the Hakím's family individually, and then said to Máni: 'What is your business with Tamízdár Bahu?'

Máni ji said: 'When she comes I will tell her.'

It was now about the time for Tamízdar to come downstairs, for it was her habit to come down after saying her afternoon prayers, and she said her sunset and evening prayers, both of them, on the lower floor.

When Máni ji *saw* Asghari she had some scruples about saying anything to her on the matter of taking service as a governess. But in the course of conversation she mentioned that the Begam sáhib was anxious to get her daughter educated, that the Begam's elder sister had spoken to her about Asghari, and that the Begam had in consequence sent *her* to the house.

Asghari said: 'Pray make many salaams on my behalf to both of the Begam sáhibs, and say that I never grudge what little knowledge I possess to anyone. The only object of study is to enable a person to benefit others, and the elder Begam sáhib is aware, no doubt, that in my old home I taught many girls to read. It would please me greatly to teach the Begam sáhib's daughter, but—what can I do? The Begam sáhib will not send her daughter here, and it is impossible for me to go there.'

Máni ji, without actually mentioning the word *salary*, said in a low voice: 'The Begam sáhib is prepared to guarantee every kind of expense, even of pocket-money.'

Asghari said: 'That is all very good of her, and moreover, it is quite in keeping with her high position. But we too—humble folk as we are, living under her shade—God does not leave us without food and clothing. I am ready to perform any service for her as an unpurchased slave. And if she wishes for a paid governess there are plenty to be found in the city.'

After this Máni ji asked some questions about Asghari, and when she learnt that she was a Tahsildár's daughter, and that Maulavi Muhammad Fázil sáhib, too, held an appointment of fifty rupees a month, she felt abashed at the impropriety of her having hinted at her taking service. But while she listened to Asghari's conversation, Máni ji became enchanted with her. Although she had been in the way of seeing semi-regal establishments, the purity of Asghari's language struck her with astonishment. She began to apologize, saying: 'Madam, pray forgive me.'

Asghari said: 'Why do you drag me over the thorns like this? In the first place, to take service is nothing wrong—there is nothing sinful in it, and besides, when you were not acquainted with the facts, what harm was there in your asking?'

After a time Máni ji took her leave, and when she got back, she said: 'Begam sáhib! she *is* a governess—one out of a hundred thousand, no doubt of that. To look at her face is enough to humanize anyone, and to sit by her side is to acquire good breeding. One might learn wisdom from being under her shadow, and catch an air of refinement from breathing her atmosphere. But she is not one to take service. She is a Tahsildár's daughter, and daughter-in-law to the agent of the Chief of Lahore. They keep a woman-servant in the house. There is a fine cloth spread in the reception-room, and the seats are covered with embroidery and cushions. They are well-to-do people living in comfort. Bless you! how should she care to take service?'

Sháh Zamáni Begám said: 'She is quite right. You sent Máni there, Sultána, dear, but I was certain myself that she would never take service.'

Máni ji said: 'But *she* is such a dear good woman that she is quite willing to teach for nothing.'

'What! and come here?' asked Sultána.

Máni ji said: 'Why, Begam sáhib, you cannot suppose that a person who has no need to take service should care to come here.'

Sultána said: 'How then? Do you mean that the child should go there?'

Sháh Zamáni said: 'Why, what harm is there is that? The house is only two steps off. And whatever makes you have such a poor idea of the Maulavi sáhib? His mother was first cousin on the father's side to our Ali Naqi Khán.'

Sultána said: 'Ah! then in one sense he belongs to our family.'

Sháh Zamáni said: 'There you are. God forbid you should think him a mere common person! In old days he was very well-to-do in the world; it is since the Chief's fortunes declined that the poor fellow has become impoverished. Still, they have always kept a woman-servant in the house, and there are one or two retainers at the entrance.'

Sultána said: 'So be it, then. Husnára shall go there.'

CHAPTER
XX

✦

Next day the two sisters, Sháh Zamáni begam and Sultána begam, called at Asghari's house, and took Husnára with them. Although the appliances at Asghari's command were of a humble character, still, by reason of her tact and good management, she arranged for their reception so successfully that everything wanted was forthcoming without any fuss. Two kinds of attar,[1] a box of unguents in four compartments, some cardamoms, prepared betelnut, and tea made their appearance with no interruption to the conversation. Some pawn leaves of excellent flavour were prepared. The two sisters said to Asghari: 'It would be such a kindness to us if you would give your mind to this girl's education.'

Asghari said: 'To begin with, it is not so very much that I have acquired myself, but what little I have acquired through the kindness of my elders, please God! I will not spare myself in explaining to her to the best of my power.'

As they were about to take leave, Sultána begam offered to put a gold mohur into Asghari's hand.

Asghari said: 'I do not want this. Surely you do not suppose it possible that I should take any fee from your honor?'

Sultána said: 'Heaven forfend! I never presumed to offer you a fee. This is for sweets for the *Bismillah*.'

Asghari said: 'Ah, yes, it is the custom to distribute sweets for good

---

[1] *i.e.*, 'Otto' of *roses*, and of some other flower.

luck at the beginning. But that won't come to a gold mohur. A pound or two of confectioneries will be ample for the children to sweeten their mouths with,' and so saying she made a sign to Diyánat, who fetched a large dish from the store closet, and filled it with comfits. Asghari herself recited the Fátiha over them, and gave some to Husnára, and then told Diyánat to take up the laden dish and distribute the rest among all the children.

Sultána said: 'My dear, you have put me to shame.'

Asghari said: 'What are we poor humble folk fit for? But whatever there is in the house is all your honor's property. One thing indeed will be my giving if I teach Husnára begam, and may God bring about the day when I shall be made proud of it by your honor!'

After this interchange of complimentary phrases Sháh Zamáni begam and Sultána begam returned home, and left Husnára behind them in Asghari's charge. I shall have to make a separate book about the manner in which Asghari conducted Husnára's education; if the whole of that story were written down here this book would be too large. But what I wish to say now is, that directly Husnára became Asghari's pupil Asghari was besieged by the whole mohulla. Every woman you see is taking her daughter to Asghari. But Asghari picked out those who were born of good parents, and found some pretext for putting off the others. She said she might any day be going to stay with her mother, and that schooling was of no good unless it were continuous. For all that, some twenty girls became regular attendants; but it was against Asghari's principles to take pay from any girl. In fact, she was in the habit of spending a rupee or two upon them out of her own allowance. From morning till noon there was reading, and then two hours' leave was granted for dinner. After dinner there was writing, and for the last three hours of the daylight needlework.

The needlework was a source of profit. For it was not merely sewing that was taught, but lace-making of every kind, and fine stitching, and all kinds of cutting out, and the making and stitching on of embroidery. At the commencement Asghari laid out ten rupees in getting together the necessary materials, but afterwards there began to be a surplus even after that expense. Whatever things the girls made Diyánat used to take privately to the bázár, and get them disposed of, and in this manner there gradually accrued quite a large sum to the credit of the school. Out of this fund clothes were made and books were purchased for those girls who were poor. A woman was retained as servant specially for the girls—to give them water, and to pull their punkah, and her wages, too, came out of the fund.

As for the girls, they used at one time to be frightened out of their wits at merely going near their governesses, but Asghari's pupils were enamoured of her. They began dropping in of their own accord, even before she had finished dressing, and stayed in a body till a watch of the night had passed, and would hardly go then. The reason of this was that Asghari had a genuine affection for all of them, and had devised such an excellent method of teaching that the children got educated in the course of conversation. There was nothing here of that sing-song drone like a spinning-wheel, which begins in the morning and is not over by sunset.[2] Asghari taught her pupils just as her father had taught herself, and hence the girls were not only the most diligent of pupils, but the most genial of companions. When any girl's marriage took place some little bit of jewellery was included among her wedding-presents at the cost of the school fund. If Asghari had desired to increase her numbers all the girls' schools in the city would have been deserted. Hundreds of women made overtures to her on behalf of their daughters, and girls too, came running themselves from all quarters, for the simple reason that in other schools there is nothing but restraint all day long, and the harshness of the governesses, and the minimum of learning with the maximum of beating and task work. Suppose they have read all day in one of those—it is but a few words; from morning to evening the same dull repetition, and if any girl is silent for a minute, and the teacher's eye falls upon her—then woe betide her! But if you inquire what sort of tasks they perform—first of all, when they arrive in the morning, they sweep out the house, then they fold up the bedding of the mistress and of the master,[3] and of some ten or twelve little monitors

[2]The ordinary method of instruction is for a monitor to read a few words of the prescribed book, which all the other children repeat together over and over again, till they get the cue for a few more words, and so on. The meaning of the words is never explained.

[3]The mistress's husband is called 'master', and their children 'monitors', sarcastically.

of the school—nay, perhaps of the mistress's neighbours; and then four or five of them together will move out of the way the big heavy bedsteads, bad luck to them![4] When that is over, some of the girls—whose ill-fate has come speedily—must sit down to their scripture lesson, and no sooner do the words fall from their lips than the teacher begins to flourish her wand. And some—who saw a good man's face when they first got up[5]—must do all the housework. One of them holds the schoolmistress's little boy; her elbow is breaking under his weight, but her neck is fiend-ridden by the dread of a beating, and so she walks up and down, beguiling the time. The cries of beaten children fall on her ears. What is throbbing inside her is her own trembling heart. She esteems her own affliction a relief from *that* torture. Another has begun burnishing yesterday's dirty cooking-pots. Already her joints are swelling, and her shoulders refuse their work; but her little sister is getting a beating, and is screaming out, 'Mercy, teacher, I am dying! Mercy, I am pledged to you! Mercy for God's sake! Mercy for the prophet's sake! Mercy! I am the monitor's handmaid. Oh! oh! mother, mother! sister, sister!' And the sister?—is here scrubbing pots as fast as she can to the tune of 'jhain jhain.'[6] Then, when they are quit of these duties, the time has come for the spices to be ground, for the meal to be kneaded, for the fire to be lit, for the meat to be browned. Then at mid-day, if you ask for the teacher—she is fast asleep, and little innocents are employed in fanning her, and in their hearts are praying to God that she may sleep so soundly as never to get up again.

That is the kind of misery which prevails in other schools.[7] But under Asghari's rule there was neither beating nor scolding. It was a great threat of hers if she said: 'Listen to me, sister, if you do not learn

[4]The bedsteads would have been moved into the open courtyard in the middle of the house for people to sleep on, and in the morning they would be set up on end in the verandas, so as to take up as little room as possible.

[5]Which is held to confer good luck for the day.

[6]The pots, which are of copper or brass, are burnished with a moist cloth covered with fine sand or ashes. Of necessity they have to be kept scrupulously clean. 'Jhain jhain' is an expression imitative of the noise made in burnishing.

[7]This book was written more than thirty years, ago, and probably has had as great an influence on public opinion in India as 'Nicholas Nickleby' had in England.

your lessons my school will get a bad name on your account. I shall send for your mother, and say to her: "Your daughter is not learning anything here: you had better place her with another governess".' No need to say more. The girl was in despair, and at the next lesson everything was on the tip of her tongue. Or suppose any girl did not remember her lesson correctly, it was said to her: 'Sister, you have not learnt your lesson today; this afternoon the other girls will do needle-work, and you reading.' That was quite enough to make her get her lesson by heart in no time.

The two monitors in the school were Mahmúda and Husnára. There was no sweeping the house, no folding up of bedclothes, no moving of bedsteads, no cleaning of dirty vessels, no carrying about of budding monitors. On the contrary, the girls had a servant of their own. It was a reign of love and peace, and only three things to work at—reading, writing, and sewing. The girls took the keenest pleasure in gaining the instruction they received.

CHAPTER

XXI

B y way of giving you some notion of the method of Asghari's teaching I insert here the following anecdote of the school.

There was a certain woman named Safíhan,[1] whose daughter Fazílat was about ten years old. This Fazílat had a natural propensity for reading and writing, and all sorts of needlework. Safíhan, on the contrary, wanted Fazílat to do all the sweeping in the house, to wash the floors, and burnish the cooking vessels. Fazílat used to chafe at any work of this description. She would do it, certainly, when her mother expostulated with her, but even then in a perfunctory manner. One day, when Safíhan had lost her temper with Fazílat, she took her off and placed her in Asghari's school, and said: 'Mistress, this daughter of mine is a useless girl. She flatly refuses to do anything that I tell her. Pray give her a training of such a kind that she may take an interest in doing her work in the house.'

When Asghari looked at the girl, she saw that she could make something of her; on the other hand, Fazílat had found in Asghari a governess after her own heart. She would come to the school at break of day, and not go home to her dinner till noon. Then, when she had finished eating her food, she would rush back again, and drink her water after she reached the school;[2] and however early she

[1] Pronounce Sufeehun, with the accent on the second syllable. The word means 'ignorant'. Fazílat (Fuzeelut) means 'pre-eminence.'

[2] It is a common expression for speed in travelling to say that one has eaten at one place and drunk water at another.

came in the afternoon, she would stay on till some time after nightfall.

Safíhan used to call at the school occasionally to see after her, and it happened several times that she found her playing at dolls with the other girls; two or three times she found her cooking dolls' feasts. One day, some time after nightfall—Fazílat being late in coming home—Safíhan went to fetch her. When she arrived at the school, what does she see but Mahmúda engaged in telling stories, and all the girls of the school sitting round her listening, and the mistress herself, too, sitting among the girls, and listening to the stories.

Then, indeed, the soul of Safíhan took flame, and burnt itself to ashes. She called out: 'My word, madam! you are a fine schoolmistress, bringing these girls to ruin! All the times I have come to see Fazílat I have never once found her reading. Call this a school! It is a regular playing-house! That is why the girls are all so eager to come here!'

Asghari said: 'Sister, if your daughter is not being educated in accordance with your wishes, it is in your power to remove her. But do not cast imputations unjustly upon the school: Tell me, now, how many days was Fazílat reading at the Má-i ji's[3] school?'

Safíhan said: 'I put her there when the moon of Míránji[4] was young. She read all through Madár, and continued reading through Khwája Mu-ínuddín. She is with you from the beginning of Rajab.'[5]

'Well,' said Asghari, 'how far had she read at the Má-i ji's?'

'During the three months,' said Safíhan, 'she read the whole of "*And the good women*",[6] and half of "*God does not love the utterance of evil words*".'

Asghari said: 'One portion and a half in three months; that is half a portion a month. Your daughter came here in Rajab, and now it is the new moon of the blank month[7]—that is four months. She has just finished the whole of "*And I do not justify myself*"—that is to say, she has read altogether seven and a half portions, and her account now

---

[3]Pronounce Má-ee jee: the word means 'mother'.

[4]She names the three months Rabiussáni, Jumádalúla, and Jumádalukhrá by the *saints* whose holidays occur in them.

[5]Pronounce Rujjub.

[6]The words between inverted commas are the opening sentences of 'portions' of the Qur-án, of which there are thirty.

[7]*i.e.,* without a saint's day. The month Shawwal.

stands at about one portion a month—double what it was at the Má-í ji's school. And when Fazílat came here, she could not even draw a straight line with ink;[8] now she writes her name, and considering her age, she does not make the letters so badly. She did not know how to count up to twenty properly, and now she can multiply by fifteen. And in sewing, she could not hem a border straight. Look at her handiwork now. Here, Aqíla! just bring me the work-basket: Show her some of Fazílat's stitching in that coat; and while you are about it, bring some of Fazílat's fancy work, edgings, fringes, flowers, embroidery, lace-work,[9] anything you can find.'

Fazílat said: 'Mistress, may not I go and fetch them?'

Fazílat ran off, and came back laden with her productions. Safíhan, who had got ten answers for every one of her doubts, was dumbfounded.

Asghari said: 'Speak out, sister. You have some idea of justice. What else did you think your daughter would learn in four months' time?'

Poor Safíhan was as much abashed as if pails of cold water had fallen on her. She did not dare look the mistress in the face. All this time Mahmúda's interesting story had been interrupted by her sudden advent. All the girls began looking at her with big reproachful eyes. She said: 'Mistress, what did I know of *this*? Fazílat stays here all day long; she comes home so late, there is only time for her to get her supper and go to bed. I never have a chance of asking her anything. On the few occasions when I have happened to come here I have found her, sometimes playing with dolls, sometimes playing at cooking, and sometimes listening to stories. That gave me the impression that she was wasting her time in play and nonsense. Forgive me the words which just now escaped my mouth.'

Asghari said: 'Certainly. Your anxiety was not unnatural. But it is in these very amusements that I teach the girls things of real use. In their games of cooking the children learn the way of preparing every kind of dish. They get to know the proportion of spices, to judge the amount of salt, and to test things by their flavour and odour. Eh, Fazílat!

[8]The first step in learning to write Persian is to practise drawing a horizontal line from right to left the whole space of the board which serves as a copy-book.

[9]Twelve different kinds of fancy work are enumerated, for which it would be impossible to find exact equivalents in English.

yesterday was Friday—tell me, what amount of *zarda*[10] did all of you girls cook together? Let us hear how it was prepared and what the account came to.'

Fazílat said: 'The accounts were all written down by Mahmúda begam in her book. But, as your honour told me, I paid particular attention to the receipt for preparing it, and I have it well in my mind. There was one seer of rice. First of all we soaked it in the large pan. I think we sent for half a pice worth of hársinghár[11] stalks, but a pice worth came. We put them to boil in about a seer and a half of water. When they came to the boil, and the colour had gone out of them, we strained them out, and threw the rice, after draining off the water, into the liquor. When the rice was half soft, and just a grain of hardness remained in it, we spread it out on a cloth, so that all the moisture might evaporate. Then we took two chitacks[12] of ghee and made it frizzle in a degchi with a seasoning of cloves, and emptied the rice into it. Then we poured over the whole an equal weight with the rice of coarse sugar, and just as much water, by guess, as would soften whatever was left hard in the rice. Then we frizzled in some ghee one chitack of raisins, and when they were well swollen, threw them into the rice; and afterwards we made it all hot with live coals above and beneath the cooking-pot.'

Asghari said: 'The ingredients are all right, but when *I* saw the rice it had got caked. I fancy that, when you spread it out on the cloth, you did not douche it with cold water.'

Then Asghari turned to Safíhan and said: 'Well, sister, did your daughter cook the *zarda* properly? That is all by favour of the dolls' feasts. And now, Mahmúda dear, let us hear the accounts of your *zarda*.'

Mahmúda went and fetched her account-book, and said: 'Mistress, rice, at six seers the rupee, one seer of it, two annas and three-quarters. The hársinghár-stalks and cloves together, one pice. Ghee, at two seers

[10]Pronounce Zurrda. It means a dish of rice coloured yellow (in rich houses with saffron).

[11]The *Nydaníhcs arbor tristis*, an unsightly shrub which produces in the night lovely flowers that are shaken off by the wind at dawn. The petals are white and the corolla a deep orange colour. The latter is used for dyeing, and instead of saffron for colouring rice.

[12]There are sixteen chitacks in a seer, so that a chitack is about two ounces.

the rupee—we ordered three chitacks; two were used with the cloves for the seasoning, and one at the finish in frizzling the raisins—altogether one anna and a half for ghee. Sugar, at four seers the rupee, one seer, four annas. Raisins, one pice. Charcoal, two annas.[13] The total came to ten annas and three pice. Ten girls shared the expense. I gave an anna and three-quarters, and—Fazílat one, Aqíla two, Husnára three, Ummatullah four, Aliya five, Sulma six, Ummunnabin seven, the two sisters Shakíla and Jamíla nine—each of them one anna.'

Asghari said: 'Mahmúda, you let yourself be cheated.'

Mahmúda reflected, and then said: 'Yes, mistress, there were some cowries over from the rice;[14] that wretched banya pocketed them. Dear me! if the stalks and the cloves had been included for that, we should have saved one pice. Run, Diyánat, and recover the cowries from the banya.'

Asghari said: 'Eh! eh! what are you about? A matter of cowries, and it happened two days ago! Say nothing about it now. It's a punishment for your mistake, to put up with a little loss like that.'

Asghari now addressed Husnára, and said: 'Now we know how the *zarda* was made, and what it cost. Tell me, what did you all do with a whole seer of *zarda* after it was cooked.'

Husnára replied: 'We put a pyramid of it on each of two middle-sized dishes, and sent them to the mosque for the poor, and with the rest we filled thirteen little plates. There are twenty-five girls in the school; one plateful was allowed for every two, but the thirteenth plate I had by myself.'

'What?' asked Asghari; 'did you take a double share?'

Husnára said: 'No, not that. I had a half-plateful. Ask any of them.'

Asghari said: 'And how did it happen that you were outside of the family?'

Husnára was silent.

---

[13]This last item is not in the original as published, but has been added to make the total correct. *Some* item must have been omitted when the work was in the press. Translator.

[14]There are 16 annas in the rupee. One-sixth of 16 annas is 2/1/3, not, as Mahmúda calculated, 2/1/4. She should have received the change in cowries for 1/12th of an anna, about equal to 1/2rd of a farthing.

Ummatullah said: 'Mistress, she is too proud to eat with all of *us*.'

Husnára said: 'No, mistress; it has not anything to do with pride. I came last of all the girls to the tablecloth; that is why I was left by myself. Let your honor ask Mahmúda begam.'

Ummatullah said: 'Why, just now, not so very long ago, you quarrelled with me over drinking the water I had left, did not you?'

'Do you call that quarrelling?' said Husnára. 'All I said was that you ought to take only so much water as you wished to drink. It *is* bad manners to leave water in a glass after drinking part of it.'

Asghari next inquired to Mahmúda: 'That book which I gave you— "A Variety of Dainty Dishes"—have you tried all the dishes in it by cooking them—or not yet?'

Mahmúda took a little time to think, and then said: 'To the best of my belief, I have had all of them cooked, and some several times over. All the elder girls know how to make the usual everyday dishes; and, besides that, there have been cooked more than once all the different kinds of pulao,[15] rissoles, pastry, fritters—sweet and savoury—cakes, and puddings and sweet-meats; and all the girls have seen them being cooked, and have lent a hand in the cooking. And as for that, your honor knows that in our school doll-feasts are only the name. Whatever we cook is fit to be served up to a well-to-do family. And—I forgot— Husnára has a fondness for making chutnies and preserves. Excepting her, these are things which the other girls do not know much about.'

After this Asghari said to Safihan: 'Sister, you will have understood by this time the use of dolls' feasts as they are practised here. It is very late now, and some of the children's homes are a good way off. If you will come tomorrow, we will let you inspect the dolls; and if you stay till the evening I will get the girls to let you hear their stories.'

Everyone then dispersed. Safihan, as she was going off, put her hands together, and said: 'For mercy's sake, mistress, forgive me my mistake!'

---

[15]Eleven different kinds of pulao are enumerated, and fourteen other dishes are named for which exact equivalents in English cannot be given.

CHAPTER
XXII

ᚬᚬᚬᚬ

O n the next day, when Safíhan arrived, Asghari showed her specimens of the girls' embroidery, and the gold stripings they had braided, the gold knobs they had twisted, the borderings and flowers they had made, and the clothes, both men's and women's, which they had cut out and sewn together, all of which excited in Safíhan, when she saw them, the utmost astonishment. After that, Asghari showed her the girls' doll-houses.

In these houses there were all the appurtenances of a household. Carpets, cushions, spittoons, basins, ewers, trunks, curtains, sunshades, ceiling-cloths, punkhas, mosquito-curtains, beds, all kinds of cooking vessels, and quite an array of ornaments, and everything properly arranged in its own place. And the dolls were dressed up exactly as if there were an assemblage of guests in a house celebrating some festival. When Safíhan had done looking at the dolls' houses, Asghari said to her: 'Of all the children's amusements, I think most highly of their dolls. By their means the girls acquire a knowledge of sewing, and stitching, and cutting out clothes, and of housekeeping, and of all kinds of ceremonial functions, such as the sixth day,[1] the taste of rice, the weaning, the first reading,[2] the first fast-keeping, the betrothal, the feasts and holidays, the creams and cakes of the Muharram, the Hindu festivals, the weddings, and all the ceremonies which occur before and

---

[1] When the *mother* first receives the congratulations of the friends admitted to see her.

[2] Elsewhere called the Bismillah.

after a wedding. Sister Safíhan, it is but a few days since your daughter began coming here, but the girls who have been with me for some time—such as, well, Ummunnabin,[3] who is sitting here, or my sister-in-law Mahmúda, or Husnára—I say it in all humility: if the management of some big, well-appointed household were committed to them at once, they could discharge it as well as the most practised and experienced woman could do. It is not only their reading which I insist upon; I try to make them *useful* for the business of the world, which will fall upon their heads before many days are over.'

After this speech Asghari called Husnára, and said: 'Sister, your dolls' house is very finely appointed. I notice only one thing amiss— your dolls do not seem to possess any coloured costumes. Perhaps you have not learnt the art of dyeing.'

Husnára said: 'Oh yes; Mahmúda begam has taught me many ways of dyeing. It was my own fancy not to dye their clothes.'

Asghari said: 'Well, tell us some colours.'

Husnára said: 'Mistress, colours for the rainy season: red, orange, pomegranate-blossom, peach-blossom, melon colour, rice-green, maroon; and for the winter: marigold colour, yellow ochre, crimson, grass green, dusky brown, purple, black, dark blue, rose colour, saffron, slate colour, light brown; and for the hot weather: light green steel colour, *campak*-colour, cotton-flower colour, almond colour, camphor white, milk white, poppy-seed colour, *fálsa*-colour, sandal wood colour, and bright red. And there are plenty of other colours beside these. I have only mentioned those which are usually worn.'

'Come, now,' inquired Asghari, 'you have enumerated the names of a great variety of colours; are we to understand that you know how to produce all of them in dyeing?'

Husnára said: 'I have only mentioned those that I myself know how to dye.'

'Well,' said Asghari, 'tell us how you dye melon colour.'

Husnara said: 'You must get half a yard of *káhi qand*,[4] of good deep colour, and, having boiled it well in water, you put in some alum and

---

[3]Pronounce Oommoonnubbeen.
[4]A coarse dyed cotton cloth imported from Turkey.

mix with it. The alum will make the colour of the *qand* come out, and then you can dye your cloth.'

'And suppose there is no *qand* procurable?' said Asghari.

Husnára said: 'Then if you boil up the flowers of the *dhák*-tree[5] and mix ground alum with them you will get melon colour, but light, more like cotton-flower colour; you cannot dye melon colour well without *qand*, and if, instead of *qand*, you get the colour out of woolen stuff, you have such a dye as you may thank Heaven for. But nowadays magenta has come so much into fashion that it beats all the other dyes; not only for clothes—the *gotas*[6] for the Muharram are coloured with magenta, and very well coloured. My elder sister sent us some *zarda* she had cooked coloured with magenta; it was better than saffron.'

Asghari Khánam asked with amazement: 'Why, Husnára, surely you never ate that rice, coloured with magenta!'

Husnára said: '*I* did not eat any; but why, mistress, is there any harm in it?'

Asghari said: 'Why, my dear, there is arsenic in magenta. Mind what you do! you should not put anything coloured with magenta on your tongue.'

Husnára said: 'In the Muharram I ate lots of *gotas* that had been coloured with it.'

Asghari said: 'What of that? It only takes the least morsel of it to colour a large number of *gotas*. That is how you came to no harm. But for all that, remember that there is poison in it.'

Husnára said: 'Why, people eat maunds of magenta-coloured sweetmeats.'

Asghari said: 'They do very wrong. Any poison, if it reaches its own climax, is certain to have its effect.'

As the evening drew on the girls, after putting carefully away all their needlework and books, came and sat down together as usual to amuse themselves, and tell stories, and ask each other riddles. Asghari said to Safíhan: 'The stories we have here are not all about cock-sparrows and hen-sparrows. We have a capital story-book containing a great variety

---

[5] *Butea frondosa.*
[6] Small cakes eaten during the Muharram.

of excellent tales, and the author has conveyed some piece of instruction in every one of them. Moreover, the language of the book is extremely refined. The girls will now divert themselves with stories out of that book. They acquire a clear elocution by rehearsing stories, and become more and more practised in the art of expressing themselves correctly; moreover, when I have leisure, I join with them, and go on putting questions to them in the middle of their stories, and they give me such answers as their reason suggests. If their answers are incorrect I explain the matter to them. And guessing riddles tends to increase their reasoning powers, and to sharpen their wits. But do you now sit down with them and look on. *I* have been summoned today by Aliya's mother. Her baby is not well, and she sent me very urgent messages to come to her. If I do not go she will take it ill of me, and besides, I could not bear myself, not to go.'

Safíhan said: 'Yes, I too have heard that her little boy has not taken his milk for days, and she, poor thing! is in terrible anxiety. Dear, dear! God grant the poor little creature may survive! He is the child of many prayers. After the years of longing God showed her this sign of His mercy. There has only been one boy since Aliya was born. Mistress, no doubt she has sent for you to find some cure for him?'

Asghari said: 'Curing is not in my province at all. But it so happened once before that the boy refused his milk; I told her of a few remedies, such as bezoar, bamboo manna, rose pollen, small cardamoms, cummin seed, cassia buds, purslain; it pleased God that the child did recover.'

Safíhan said: 'Mistress, you are crammed full of every virtue!'

Asghari said: 'What virtue is there in that? At my mother's home they bestow a deal of thought upon the different medicines. When I was a child I used to clarify and make up whatever drugs came to the house, and paid some attention to it. In that way I have a few hearsay prescriptions by heart, and I have told them to anyone who was in need of them. Women, as a rule, are the people who *have* to prescribe for the ailments of children. But when such a crisis as this befalls them they take them to a hakím.'

Safíhan said: 'Mistress, you have been so kind as to show me all the arrangements of your school; for Heaven's sake, put off going, just for a moment, so that I may see how the girls tell their stories, and how you manage to teach them as the stories are going on.'

Asghari said: 'Sister, I am already very late, but still, it is for your sake. Well, whose turn is it today of the girls?'

Mahmúda said: 'It is Ummatullah's turn; but why not make Fazílat recite?'

Asghari said: 'Very well, Fazílat, tell us some short story.'

Fazílat began to recite: 'There was a certain king—'

Asghari asked: 'Whom do they call "king"?'

Fazílat said: 'A man—like Bahádur Sháh was in Delhi.'

Asghari: 'Your description is such as anyone might understand, *if only* he was acquainted with Delhi and with Bahádur Sháh.'

Fazílat: 'They call a man "king" if he is a ruler.'

Asghari: 'Then the chief officers of the police are kings?'

Fazílat: 'No, *they* are not kings, they are the king's servants.'

Asghari: 'How? Is not the chief constable of the city a ruler?'

Fazílat: 'He is a ruler, but a king is ruler above all, and issues orders to all.'

Asghari: 'Who is our king?'

Fazílat: 'Since the English arrested Bahádur Sháh, and transported him, there is not any king.'

All the girls burst out laughing when they heard this.

Asghari said: 'Fazílat, you are very dull. You have said yourself that if anyone is the biggest ruler, and gives order to all, he is king, and you are aware that the English arrested Bahádur Sháh and transported him; then have the English become king or not?'

Fazílat: 'Yes, they have become king. I suppose so.'

Asghari: 'Well, then, tell us who is our king.'

Fazílat: 'The English.'

Asghari: 'What, is "The English" the name of any particular person?'

Fazílat: 'No, there are hundreds and thousands of English.'

Asghari: 'Then are all the English kings?'

Fazílat: 'What else?'

When they heard this the girls laughed again.

Asghari beckoned to Husnára, and said: 'You give the answer.'

Husnára said: 'Mistress, our king is Queen Victoria.'

Asghari: 'A man or a woman?'

Husnára: 'A woman.'

Asghari: 'Where does she live?'

Husnára: 'In London.'

Asghari: 'Where is London?'

Husnára: 'It is a very large city in the country of the English.'

Asghari: 'How far off is it?'

Husnára: 'I read in a book that it is five thousand kos.'

Asghari: 'And how much is a kos?'[7]

Husnára: 'Mistress, they call it three kos to the tomb of Nizámuddín.'[8]

Mahmúda laughed now, and said: 'A kos is one thousand seven hundred and sixty yards.'

Asghari asked Mahmúda: 'Do you remember that time when I went to the Qutb sáhib,[9] and you went with me, and saw there were stones sunk into the road at moderate distances, and there was something written on them—what kind of stones were those?'

Mahmúda: 'I supposed that they were the stones to mark the koses, but the carriage went so fast that I could not steady my eyes to look at them; I was not well able to read what was written on them.'

Asghari: 'Those were not kos stones; they were mile-stones. A mile is the half of a kos, and there is a stone fixed at each mile, and there is written on it that from here to Delhi is so many miles, and to the Qutb so many.'

Asghari then turned to Husnára again, and asked: 'Yes, sister, and in which direction is London?'

Husnára: 'It is in the north.'

Asghari: 'Is that country hot or cold?'

Husnára: 'I do not know *that.*'

Mahmúda: 'It is very cold. The further north you go the less heat there is, and as you go south the heat becomes greater and greater.'

Safíhan: 'I say, mistress, is a *woman a king*?'

Asghari: 'What is there to be astonished at in that?'

Safíhan: 'Eh! not to be astonished at? What can she do if she is a woman?'

---

[7]Pronounce like the first four letters of 'coast'.

[8]A celebrated saint whose tomb is outside Delhi.

[9]The great minaret so called. Pronounce Kootub.

Asghari: 'She does exactly the same things that men do who are kings. She governs the country; she protects her subjects.'

Safíhan: 'What is a *woman* to do? It will be the English who do it all. Probably they have made a woman king for the sake of the name.'

Asghari: 'All these English are the Queen's servants. Each has his own duty, and each has a separate amount of authority. All are bent on doing their special work to the best of their ability. And when it is *men* who are *kings*, even then their ministers and officials transact all the business.'

Safíhan: 'I cannot bring myself to believe that a woman by nature can do king's work.'

Asghari: 'Have you never heard of the Begam of Bhopál?'

Safíhan: 'Heard of her! of course I have. My own father-in-law is in service in Bhopál.'

Asghari: 'Well, then, you may look at it in this way. Bhopál is a tiny little country, and Queen Victoria rules over a large Empire. Just as the Begam of Bhopál administers her little territory, so does Queen Victoria direct the affairs of her great Empire. Bhopál is a small state; the officials are few, and they draw small salaries. Queen Victoria's Government is one of very lofty rank, with huge establishments, and lakhs of officials drawing high pay.'

Safíhan: 'Say, has the Queen any husband?'

Asghari: 'Yes, but against death there is none whose strength may prevail. God has set a blot even upon the moon. It is some years now since the Queen became a widow.'

Safíhan: 'Has the Queen any children?'

Asghari: 'Yes, god preserve them! heirs of all kinds—sons and grandsons, and daughters' daughters.'

Safíhan: 'Say, why does the Queen not come to this country?'

Asghari: 'She has a large territory there too. She has not leisure from her duties there. But the Queen's son is coming here shortly.[10] Great preparations are being made. So I saw in the papers.'

Safíhan: 'Say, what can the Queen know about this place, living thousands of kos away?'

---

[10]This refers to the Duke of Edinburgh's visit.

Asghari: 'She knows every little thing. Why not? Day and night news is travelling to her by post and by the telegraph. Thousands of newspapers go to Europe.'

Safíhan: 'How could I manage to see the Queen?'

Asghari: 'How can I tell? But at all events you can see her portrait.'

Safíhan: 'Well, if I could only see *that!*'

Asghari: 'Sister, are you saying this to make me laugh? Have you never seen a rupee?'

Safíhan: 'Of course I have.'

Asghari: 'The lady's face which appears on that is the Queen's likeness. It is on all the postage stamps. But I possess another very excellent portrait of the Queen. Some Englishman gave it to my father, and he sent it to me. Mahmúda, would you just bring me my box?'

Asghari took the picture out of her box, and showed it, and all the children gazed with the utmost delight upon the portrait of *The Queen*.

Safíhan: 'What a lovely picture! There is the Queen standing like life.'

Asghari: 'Yes, indeed. This portrait is an exact likeness of the Queen. Put it by the side of the coin, and look—what a difference! This likeness is not made by hand. There is a sort of looking-glass upon which they put some preparation, and then hold it opposite. All of itself the reflection, just as it is, is taken off upon it.'

Safíhan: 'Husnára said that London was five thousand kos off. To go from here to there must take travellers several years.'

Asghari: 'No, they reach it in a month easily across the sea.'

Safíhan: 'Dear, dear! do you have to go by sea? What hearts these English people have! Are they not afraid of the sea? Why, it makes all my hair stand on end to hear the name of the sea.'

Asghari: 'What is there to be frightened at? You go comfortably on board a ship, and there is a fine beautiful flying-car ready-made for you.'

Safíhan: 'Oh, mistress, the wretched danger there is of drowning! I tell you, it only happened last year—my mother-in-law's sister went to Mecca with the Nawáb Qutbuddin Khán. She departed in such an evil hour that she never had the good luck to return.'

Asghari: 'Yes, it depends on circumstances. Now and again it does happen that a ship founders. And if, God forbid! they foundered every day, no one would think of travelling by sea. But now the sea routes are more frequented even than the land routes. Thousands and lakhs of ships are constantly going and coming. The English, and their wives, and their children, and all the English goods—everything comes here by sea.'

Safíhan: 'What talk is there of English woman? They are altogether a different kind of women. How are *we* to take after them? They gad about outside the house. I hear they send their little tiny children to Europe, and their hearts are not distressed. Goodness knows what kind of mothers they are; whence they derive comfort for their souls. But there you are—they go about out of doors, and they have hearts of iron; what is the sea to *them*? It would be nothing difficult for them to fly in the air.'

Asghari: 'When you talk of their gadding abroad you must remember that in their country the custom of the purdah does not exist. In the Mutiny time our family took refuge in a village[11] where there was no custom of the purdah; all the young married girls went about outside the house. But—I lived there four whole months, and I observed such a modesty and propriety of demeanour among those women—going about as they did, as I would that God might grant to us women of the purdah. And why should you infer from their sending their children to Europe that they have no love for them? True, the love which these women have is tempered with reason. It is not a mad fondness like that of mothers here, who prevent their children from reading, and deny them the chance of acquiring any accomplishments. You may call that love, but in reality they are sowing thorns for their children to reap. They allow their children to grow up ill-disciplined, and bring discredit upon the very name of love.'

When the discussion had reached this point there was silence on all sides, and Fazílat again commenced repeating her story. 'The king had no son; his only child was a daughter. Giving heed to the fact that after him his daughter would be sole heir to the kingdom, he had her well instructed in reading and writing; he took pains to teach her the laws and regulations under which the country was governed,

---

[11]Probably a Ját village.

and he entrusted to *her* the business of the state in his own lifetime ...''

Fazílat had only got so far when Asghari said: 'Sister, you are rattling on with your story at a great rate, and I have a whole heap of questions to ask you in my mind; but—I am helpless. The daylight is drawing to a close, and it is absolutely necessary for me to go to Aliya's house. It is against the rule to visit a sick person at anyone's house after daylight. I cannot stay a minute longer, but you girls may go on with your stories by yourselves.' And then she said to Safíhan: 'God bless you, sister, I am going. You may sit here as long as you like now, or come here again tomorrow. The same thing goes on here every day.'

Accordingly Asghari Khánam set off on her visit to Aliya's house. Safíhan was so enraptured that she stayed on sitting with the girls until a watch of the night had gone. After Asghari Khánam's departure Mahmúda and Husnára raised many an interesting discussion as the story proceeded.

From this narrative you may gain a very fair notion of the discipline which prevailed in Asghari's school, and of her methods of instruction. It goes without saying that Asghari was very fond of Husnára, though still more so of her own sister-in-law Mahmúda. So admirably was Husnára taught by her that in two years' time she commenced the study of Persian, and conducted all her correspondence herself in the vernacular. Nothing was left now of her old peevishness and pugnacity. She had become a very gentle, studious, accomplished, and lovable daughter: And through Asghari's good offices it pleased God to restore the home of Jamálára, which had been lost to her so many years. All of that story will be written in another book, but the gist of it here is that the Hakímji's whole family, old and young alike, were ready to kiss the dust off Asghari's feet. Sultána begam devised a thousand plans for remunerating her, but this handmaid of God refused to take any gratuity When Husnára's marriage was about to take place the elder Hakím sáhib brought Maulavi Muhammad Fázil's pressure to bear on her, and gave her a pair of jewelled bracelets valued at a thousand rupees. In doing this he said: 'Listen to me, my dear: you are the same to me as one of my granddaughters; I do not make you this present as a governess, but because I regard you as a child of my own.' On his side the Maulavi sáhib reassured her, and at last Asghari accepted the bracelets.

CHAPTER
XXIII

❧

I now enter upon a new phase of my story. We have seen Asghari busily occupied with her school. But Muhammad Kámil all this time was getting bored merely for want of employment. One day he broached the subject to Asghari, and said: 'I am weary to death of this kind of life; if you approve I would like to go to the hills, to the Tahsildár sáhib, and look out for some Government appointment under his auspices.'

Asghari took a little time to reflect, and then said: 'Certainly, it is most important that you should get some appointment, for you see yourself what narrow means we have to keep the house with. My dear father-in-law is now an old man, and it would only be right for him to stay at home, and for you to be earning some money, and doing your duty by him. Besides that, Mahmúda is growing to be a big girl. I am looking forward to her betrothal, and it is my wish that she should marry into a family of very high rank. Indeed, I have a scheme for her in my head. Please God, her betrothal shall be arranged before another year is over. But for that we shall require a host of preparations, and up to now there is not a thing ready of any kind. Your dear brother—to begin with, he has left the family roof; but anyhow, his salary is so small that he can barely make both ends meet—what can he give to others? There is no help for it that I can see, except that you should take service. Still, I do not like the idea of your going to the hills. Of course my father will do his utmost for you, and it is not unlikely that some good post would be found for you pretty quickly, but to hold an appointment by clinging to the support of someone else is not the correct thing. A man's earnings, no matter how small, should be those of his own right arm. Although my father is not a stranger, and in the chain of relationship his hand is loftier than you, so that there is no harm—I don't say in *accepting*—there is none in asking—his assistance; still, may God preserve you from being under an obligation to *any* one! That makes the eyes downcast for ever. Suppose that *he* has never said a word about it, there are a hundred others in the family (God keep it!) who won't say anything to your face perhaps, but will certainly talk behind your back—"Ah, there goes the man who got his appointment through his father-in-law!"'

Muhammad Kámil said: 'What shall I do, then? Shall I go to Lahore?'

Said Asghari: 'What *is* there at Lahore? The Chief's own fortune is ruined. It is a marvel how he can give your father, with all his regard for his past services, as much even as fifty rupees a month. There is no room at his court for a new-comer.'

'Well,' said Muhammad Kámil, 'there are plenty of other courts.'

'Since the English rule was established,' said Asghari, 'all the native chiefs are much in the same state of decay. Although they all keep up something of their former grandeur, and a few representatives of the old days are to be found still clinging on to them, yet, after all, what is it but dust? Their salaries are in arrear for years.'

'Well,' said Muhammad Kámil, 'something must be done. What is it?'

'Look out for some appointment under the English Government,' was Asghari's reply.

Muhammad Kámil said: '*Those* appointments are not to be had without interest and favour. Why, there are thousands of men, far better than I, who are wandering about in despair, and no one asks after them.'

'Yes,' said Asghari, 'that is true enough. But when a man once determines upon any course of action he must leave the issue to God, and not admit a thought of despondency into his mind. Granted there are thousands of men wandering about vainly in search of employment, still, the men who do hold government appointments are men just like yourself, and one thing, which is equal to a hundred, is this, that men get them by decree of Providence. Very able men are longing for work, and are left in the lurch, and yet, if it be God's will to give— it is no question of interest or ability—He breaks through the roof and gives. People send for them to their homes, and confer appointments upon them.'

'Then,' said Muhammad Kámil, 'the upshot of it is that I should stay at home and do nothing?'

'No, indeed,' said Asghari, 'that is not my meaning at all. A man must use his own endeavours, necessarily, as far as he can do anything of himself.'

Muhammad Kámil said: 'But that is just the difficulty. What sort of efforts am I to make?'

Asghari said: 'Get acquainted with the officials here. Make friends with as many of them as you can. By their means you will be kept informed of any appointment that is going, and with their help you may obtain access to one of the Hákims.'[1]

Muhammad Kámil acted on this advice, and began to cultivate the acquaintance of the different officials. Gradually he was to be found calling upon such personages as the Tahsildár and Sarrishtadár. From his paying court to them it became known to everyone that he too was a candidate for Government employ; and at length Banda Ali Beg, who was a deposition writer in the Kachahri,[2] one day said to him: 'Young gentleman, if you are seeking Government employment, come to Kachahri every day with me. Be an apprentice for a time, and acquire some practical knowledge of the work; let the Hákims get to know your face. In that way something or other will turn up one of these days.'

Muhammad Kámil began to attend Kachahri, and to assist Banda Ali Beg with his work. In time he came to submit the papers requiring signature to the European officers, who began to know him by sight. During this time he was allowed to act more than once as a substitute

[1] Hákim, 'a man in power,' was the term usually applied to *European* officials at the date of the story.

[2] Otherwise written 'Cutcherry'. The word means an office of any kind, but is especially used of the Courts of Law.

for one or other of the lower grade officials. If any of these were obliged
to take leave he would name Muhammad Kámil as his substitute, and
give him one-half or one-third of his pay. Till one day it so happened
that a diary writer on ten rupees a month went away on three months'
leave, and at the end of the three months sent in his resignation. Maulavi
Muhammad Kámil was appointed permanently to the post.

In his conversations with Asghari, whenever the subject of his
appointment cropped up, Muhammad Kámil always spoke of it with
contempt. 'What a trumpery service!' he would say, 'grinding all day
long, and ten rupees a month! No takings on the sly; no hope of future
promotion. I shall give it up.'

These and such-like vagaries Asghari would invariably reprove. 'You
show a terrible amount of ingratitude,' she would say; 'have you forgotten those days when it was not your good fortune to be even an
apprentice? Or, now that you have made so good a start, do you begin
to misprize it? Is ten rupees a month so little? and you living comfortably at home? Look at your elder brother, who held on for years in a
merchant's office on ten rupees a month. And if you are so discon-
tented with your post, what kind of work, save the mark, will they get
out of you? The end of it will be that the place will give *you* up. Besides,
it is from small beginnings in this way that big pay comes. My father
was a copyist at first on eight rupees a month. Now, by god's grace, he
is a Tahsildár, and if it please God he will get higher promotion still.
As for takings on the sly, don't hanker after such a source of income
even in your dreams. Ill-gotten gains bring no prosperity. A man *can*
have nothing beyond what has been allotted to him by God. Why,
then, should he suffer his own integrity of purpose to be capsized? If
there is more to come to him than what he is getting now, God can
provide it for him of that which is lawful.'

In short, it was Asghari's task to keep Muhammad Kámil up to the
mark, and this went on until one day the English officer under whom
Muhammad Kámil worked was transferred to Siyálkot. This gentleman
had shown Muhammad Kámil much kindness. On the evening of
the day when the news was first made known at Kachahri, Muhammad
Kámil came home in a lamentable state of depression.

Asghari asked him: 'Is all well? why are you so sad today?'

Muhammad Kámil answered: 'What am I to say? James sáhib has been transferred to Siyálkot. He was the one man who treated me kindly. Now I shall have no more pleasure in attending Kachahri.'

For some time Asghari kept silence. By-and-by she said: 'No doubt James sáhib's transfer is a thing to be grieved at, but not to such an extent as you are carrying your grief. Someone else will come in his place, and whoever it is God will put mercy into his heart also. It is not for man to place his confidence in man.'

Presently Asghari asked: 'When will James sáhib leave?'

Muhammad Kámil said: 'He is to start by dawk garry tomorrow evening.'

Asghari said: 'You have not been to his bungalow, have you?'

Muhammad Kámil said: 'What is the use of going there now?'

'Well,' said Asghari, 'you *are* a queer man! This is just the very time to go. If nothing else comes of it he will give you some letter or certificate before he goes.'

'All right,' said Muhammad Kámil, 'I will go tomorrow morning.'

CHAPTER
XXIV

✦

Muhammad Kámil dressed himself betimes in the morning, and took his way to Mr. James's bungalow. Mr. James said to him: 'Muhammad Kámil, I am going to Siyálkot now. I liked you very much. If you care to go, come to Siyálkot with me. I will give you a place there; or if not, I will give you fifteen rupees a month out of my own pocket.

Muhammad Kámil thought for a while, and said: 'I will present myself again to your highness, and bring my answer. But first I must ask my mother.'

Accordingly, when Muhammad Kámil came home again, he reported: 'James sáhib wants to take me with him.' His mother, when she heard these words, raised an outcry, and Asghari too was aghast. After a time Muhammad Kámil asked them: 'Well, ladies, what answer shall I take back to him?'

His mother said: 'What *now?* why would you take any answer at all? Will he be waiting there for you? or has he sent any constable after you?'

Muhammad Kámil said: 'No, madam, but I gave him a promise. He will say to himself: "What selfish people these Hindustanis are! he told me a lie when I was going away."'

His mother said: 'Well, go and tell the sáhib that your going away with him is impossible.'

Muhammad Kámil asked Asghari: 'And you, lady, what is your advice?'

Asghari said: 'Advice is one thing, and the heart's desire is another.

My heart's desire is that you should stay here. You are the only person left to look after the family, and, whatever people may say, there should be some man in a house. But if you ask my *advice*, it is right for you to go. When a Hákim unasked himself invites you to go with him, it is certain that he will treat you handsomely when he reaches his destination.'

Muhammad Kámil said: 'What! a journey of two or three hundred kos for the sake of five rupees extra! *I* have no particular desire to go. It is the old proverb: "Half at home, not all abroad".'

Asghari said: 'Of course, the decision rests with you. But a chance of this kind has been sent you by Providence; it won't come again. And who is there who does not go away from home? My father—your father—why, they have spent most of their lives in foreign places. And five rupees is what we hear now; later on you will see how many the five are. Anyhow, if you don't go, you must not let people see you any more in low spirits at getting ten rupees.'

Muhammad Kámil said: 'I had better send in my resignation here, then, at once. But suppose after all nothing has turned up there. I shall have been a loser in both places.'

'In the first place,' said Asghari, 'it is against all common sense to suppose that nothing will turn up there. A great Hákim like James sáhib—and he wants to give you employment, and yet cannot see his way to it. That is beyond my comprehension. And why send in your resignation? Take leave for a month or two.'

Muhammad Kámil said: 'Yes, of course, leave is sanctioned at a moment's notice.'

Asghari said: 'What difficulty will there be about its being sanctioned? You have only to speak to James sáhib; he will write a letter.'

In short, Asghari put the yoke on Muhammad Kámil by force, and made him inclined to go. She gave him out of her own money fifty rupees in cash, and got half a dozen new suits of clothes made up for him. And she engaged Diyánat's son Rafíq to accompany him. Maulavi Muhammad Kámil went off in state to Siyálkot.

On her part Asghari wrote an account of all this in a letter to Maulavi Muhammad Fázil, and she added the following words: 'On his way to Siyálkot, James sáhib is sure to pass through Lahore. If it can be managed that your honor should meet him there, and get the Chief too to say a word of recommendation, it will be of great advantage.'

The Maulavi sáhib looked out for Mr. James, and since the Chief possessed some villages in the Siyálkot district, he sent an official letter of welcome, and arranged that Mr. James should break his journey for one night at the Chief's villa residence. After dinner, when the Chief and Mr. James were sitting together engaged in conversation, the Maulavi sáhib addressed Mr. James, and said: 'The people of Delhi are in great sorrow at being deprived of your honor's presence. Although your honor remained there as Hákim for two years only, your justice and your consideration for the feelings of the better classes had given great satisfaction to all the residents. A son of your humble servant was in attendance there upon your honor. His letters kept us informed of every circumstance.'

'What!' asked the sáhib, 'was one of your honor's sons in my Kachahri?'

The Maulavi sáhib replied: 'Muhammad Kámil.'

'Why, he is coming with me,' said the sáhib. 'Is he your son?'

'Your honor's slave,' said the Maulavi.

Here the Chief took up the cue, and said to Mr. James: 'The Maulavi sáhib is a very old servant of my state, and his advancement is in every way an object of my sincere desire, but, as your honor is aware, I have no resources left. Hence, if your honor should be pleased to befriend his son, you will be laying myself under an obligation.'

Mr. James was already well disposed towards Muhammad Kámil. The Chief's intervention was so well timed that it sank deep into his mind. Muhammad Kámil had now acquired all these claims upon his notice: first, he was young; secondly, of good birth; thirdly, recommended by the chief; fourthly, attached to the sáhib's own person; and, fifthly, a man of ability. On the very first day that Mr. James took his seat in Kachahri he appointed Muhammad Kámil to be Ná-ib Sarrishtadár[1] on fifty rupees a month, and he wrote in a letter to

[1]Ná-ib means 'deputy'. A Sarrishtadár is the head of the whole vernacular department in an office.

Maulavi Muhammad Fázil sáhib: 'At present I have given your son an appointment of fifty rupees a month, but before long I hope to promote him; your honor will kindly inform the Chief of this.'

The Maulavi sáhib duly sent a letter of thanks couched in suitable terms; and Muhammad Kámil—the man who not so long ago had been begging for an apprenticeship; who had been glad to work as a substitute for petty officials; who became a diary writer on ten rupees, and was induced only by Asghari's persuasions to accompany Mr. James to Siyálkot on a promise of fifteen—that same Muhammad Kámil was now installed at a minute's notice into a post of fifty rupees a month. Even his mother, though she had been so disheartened at the outset, was radiant with delight when she heard of the fifty rupees. The prosperity in the house was fourfold. Asghari's management, and sixty rupees coming in instead of the former twenty—what more could they ask for? As it happened, however, within that very year Muhammad Kámil became Sarrishtadár.[2] Alas! up to the date of his getting *that* appointment he kept his head; his remittances to the family arrived regularly; his letters followed quickly one after another. But—after all, he was a young man and he was living under no restraint but his own; evil company beset him, and he went astray. There began to be a falling off in his letters. Asghari, who had plenty of common-sense, perceived that there was something wrong somewhere. For many days she considered anxiously what plan she could devise; at last she came to the conclusion that there was no other course for her to take but to go to him herself.

[2]When his pay would be doubled.

CHAPTER
XXV

❦

Although Asghari had fully made up her mind that she would go to Siyálkot, she sent for Tamásha Khánam to take counsel with her, and told her all the circumstances. Tamásha Khánam said: 'Sister, has one of us gone mad? The idea of your leaving the city to go wandering about to Siyálkot!'

Asghari said: 'What have I to do with the city? My city is where *he* is with whom my life is bound up.'

'Dear, dear!' said Tamásha Khánam, 'and what will all the relations say? No one out of our family has ever gone away from home to this day.'

Asghari said: 'There is nothing for them to be shocked at. And, after all, what will they say? Why, "If she has gone to her husband, what harm has she done"? that's all. And if you talk about the family custom—well, in former days there was no dawk, nor railways, nor were the roads frequented with passengers; it was a very difficult matter for women to travel—*that* is why they did not move about. But now, what difficulty is there? I take my place in the dawk today, and, if God speed me, the day after tomorrow I am at Siyálkot. It is as though I went to Meerut.'

Tamásha Khánam asked: 'Has any letter come requesting you to go?'

'No,' said Asghari, 'no letter has come.'

Tamásha Khánam said: 'It is not proper for you to go without being asked.'

Asghari said: 'You look to what is proper and improper, and I tell you that if I do not go my *home* will be wrecked for my whole lifetime.'

Tamásha Khánam said: 'My dear sister, why do you abase yourself like this? What does *he* matter to *you*? God keep your school safe, you can provide food for ten mouths.'

Asghari said: 'My goodness, do you look at it in that light? Why, I founded the school merely for my own amusement; it was never my object to make money out of it. God knows, whether you will credit it or not—I have not spent a single pice of the school money upon myself to this day. Fifty rupees in cash, and twenty for clothes, I certainly did give to your cousin, when he was going to Siyálkot—no more, and *that* is entered as a loan; and for the rest, I have an account of every cowrie written down. Why, look you, are women's earnings any earnings at all? If families are to be reared upon women's earnings, why should there be men? Let my own hearth rest happy, and I would not trouble over ten such schools being ruined.'

Tamásha Khánam said: 'But how are you to travel now in the middle of the rains? Wait for the cold weather, and then think about it when there is a clear sky.'

'Ah me!' said Asghari, 'it is the waiting that I dread. What can be done *now* by a little expostulation will never be accomplished hereafter by endless controversies.'

Tamásha Khánam said: 'Dear, dear! does not your heart ache, sister, at the thought of leaving your family?'

'Of course it aches,' said Asghari. 'Am not I a woman? But which is better—to fret for a while at present, or to be in purgatory for a whole lifetime?'

Tamásha Khánam said: 'Have you got permission from your mother-in-law?'

Asghari said: 'You think she is likely to give it? But my mother-in-law, poor dear! is a simple-minded soul. When I make her understand, I am certain she will not detain me.'

As a matter of course Asghari did explain to her mother-in-law what her intention was, and what causes had led up to it. The thing was quite reasonable; who could find anything to say against it? The date of Asghari's departure was fixed. She went one day and explained things briefly to her own mother, and took leave of her. As for the school, she instructed the girls that she was going away only for a couple of months, that Mahmúda was quite competent to go on teaching them, and that they might all continue to attend as usual.

In the course of paying her farewell visits she went to her sister's house. Muhammad Aqil asked her: 'Well, brother Tamízdár bahu, so you are going away; what are you going to do with the school when you go?'

Asghari replied: 'I bequeath the school and the house, both of them, to your honor's care.'

Muhammad Aqil said: 'That is a fine thing to say. I have no connection with the house, nor any interest in the school. What can I do for either of them.'

Asghari said: 'It is in your honor's discretion to keep up the connection or not to keep it.'

'Such a speech as that,' said Muhammad Aqil, 'is not becoming to your lips, Tamízdár bahu. You know well enough what choice I have in the matter. The home—I was made to abandon by your elder sister; and as for the school, it is a girl's school; if it were a school for boys I would willingly undertake to teach all of them.'

Asghari said: 'Why should not my elder sister, and your honor too, come home with me now, and live there? The dear mother is all alone.'

Muhammad Aqil said: 'You must talk over your *sister.*'

Asghari said: 'What need is there? My elder sister herself understands, and is reasonable. You are not comfortable here all by yourselves. There is no one to undertake the children or to look after the house. Sorrow and joy go hand in hand with everyone. It is not the right thing to keep aloof from your friends if it can be avoided. And those old stories are things of the past. Why should there be any discord in the family, and what is the sense of keeping up an old quarrel?'

Akbari had tasted quite enough of the pleasures of separate housekeeping by this time, and was only seeking some excuse for anyone to ask them back again to live with the family. She lost no time in expressing her assent, and Asghari took both of them back with her to the house. Muhammad Kámil's mother, who had been overwhelmed with grief at the thought of Asghari's leaving her, was comforted by the reflection that she still had another daughter-in-law to take her place. Mahmúda, indeed, was under great apprehension of what might happen, but Asghari cheered her up, and assured her that Akbari's temper was no longer what it used to be. At the same time she warned her elder sister that Mahmúda was now grown up, and that she must take care not to make any rude speeches to her. As for the school, she contented herself with explaining to Muhammad Aqil that Mahmúda would carry on all the instruction and such matters if he would only keep an eye on the external arrangements, and see that Mahmúda entered the accounts of the school fund regularly in the book.

The day came for Asghari to depart. She got into her dawk garry, and arrived at Siyálkot without any delay on the road. Muhammad Kámil was intensely astonished at her sudden arrival. He said to her: 'Is all well? You have not quarrelled with my mother, have you?'

Asghari said: 'For shame! What! is your dear mother upon an equality with me that I should presume to quarrel with her? Or during these four years have you ever seen me quarrel either with her or anyone else?'

Now Muhammad Kámil had quite let himself adrift at Siyálkot, and had fallen into the worst kind of society. A crowd of toadies had assembled round him in whose hands he was a perfect fool. Bribery was rife. He had no scruples left even against nautches and dissolute plays. His surroundings were luxurious, and his ordinary expenditure amounted to four times his pay. If this state of things had lasted a very little longer it must needs have excited Mr. James's suspicion, and in the end Muhammad Kámil's appointment would have been lost to him. Asghari arrived in the very nick of time. She at once set to work to stop up all the leaks, and she took him to task severely, saying: 'God has given you an appointment of a hundred rupees a month. Is this your way of thanksgiving that you cannot be contented even with that?'

Muhammad Kámil said: 'If a man gives me anything of his own free will what is the harm?'

Said Asghari: 'I extol the perfection of God![1] Is *money* a thing that

---

[1] *i.e.*, 'in that He has created a man capable of making so silly a use of the reason with which He endowed him.'

anyone will give away of his own free will without a reason? Why, men have such a craving for money nowadays that they take no care even for their own honour, but they will not lose hold of a rupee. A man may form a guess of that from his own practice when he considers how much he is by way of giving to anyone. It is only the compulsory religious almsgiving[2] which is still observed. Out of every hundred— once a year—the fortieth part—two and a half rupees—and giving that takes the breath away. Where have the people got any such Korah's[3] treasure-chest brimming over with money that they should come and give it you without any object? It is when they see their affairs are going wrong—if they don't give something their case will be spoilt— then, in despair, they go and borrow money, or sell their wives' jewels, and give bribes.'

Muhammad Kámil said: 'I don't take the money myself. There is nothing to be afraid of.'

Said Asghari: 'In the first place, bribery never can be hushed up. But, apart from that, and if we take it for granted that it has escaped the notice of men, God, who sees all that is hidden, *He* has known of it. That His servants should heap up sins, and aggravate the indictment they must answer at the last day, argues a great fearlessness.'

By exhortations of this kind whenever she had a chance Asghari got Muhammad Kámil to repent of his evil ways. After she had been there some little time, she one day asked her husband: 'Who are those four men for whom meals are sent out of the house every day?'

Muhammad Kámil said: 'They are applicants for service. Poor fellows! they are strangers here. I told them they might live at my expense until they could get some appointment.'

'And has not any appointment been found for them yet?' asked Asghari.

Muhammad Kámil said: 'There are appointments, but not up to their social rank.'

Said Asghari: 'When their condition has come to this, that they are feeding themselves at another man's expense, what question is there left

---

[2]Called 'zakát,' the fortieth part of the year's profits, which every Musalman is bound to give in charity at the very least.

[3]Qárún, the Korah of the Bible (Num. xvi.), is supposed to have been a miser, with vast hoarded wealth.

of their social standing? Let them do any work they can get, small or great.'

Muhammad Kámil said: 'God knows what you are saying! How can they do anything derogatory to their dignity?'

'What?' said Asghari; 'is there a loss of dignity in their taking a low-grade appointment, and no loss of dignity in sponging upon another person's earnings? If these people have not even that amount of self-respect, you may be sure that their other habits are perverted. It is not good to have them about you. Depend upon it, they, too, are taking whatever they can get in *your* name. Tell them they must either accept some appointment, or be off.'

Muhammad Kámil replied: 'It would be a slur on my generosity if I were to send them away.'

Asghari said: 'When there is no generosity in them, why should *you* make a point of being generous? If we have more money than we want, there are plenty of poor people in the family who have a prior claim. What is the use of giving to strangers? and, above all, to such strangers as these? There is no necessity for you to dismiss them with harshness. You can make them understand in some way or other.'

Now, the real fact of the matter was that these very people were Muhammad Kámil's evil geniuses. By judicious management Asghari succeeded in having them turned out. Those of the servants who were ill-conducted were got rid of one by one. Asghari stayed there for a year and a half, and put everything inside and outside the house into proper order. By that time, Miyán Muslim's marriage was about to take place. A letter was sent to summon Asghari to the ceremony, and Tamásha Khánam wrote to her an urgent appeal. Since a great many days had passed, Asghari made up her mind to return to Delhi. But she thought to herself that it would never do to leave Muhammad Kámil solitary. She said to Muhammad Kámil: 'It is not the right thing for you to be alone at this distance from home. There certainly ought to be some member of the family with you; and, in my opinion, you might well send for your cousin on the mother's side, Muhammad Sálih. He will learn office work with you here while he is continuing his studies, and possibly some place may be found for him.'

A letter was despatched to Amír begam, and while Asghari was still at Siyálkot Muhammad Sálih arrived. This lad was worthy and amiable in the highest degree, and only two years junior to Muhammad Kámil. Asghari's mind was now set at rest, and having bid adieu to Siyálkot, she arrived at Lahore. Here she broke her journey for a whole week at the house of Maulavi Muhammad Fázil sáhib.

The Maulavi was now nearly sixty years old, and the business of his agency involved great labour. What with attending the different courts of justice, and looking after the Chief's cases, every day without fail, and then visits morning and evening to the various officials—when the poor Maulavi sáhib came home at night he was quite worn out with fatigue. Asghari said to him: 'Father dear, your honor's age is not equal to all this toil now. The time has come for your honor to think about retiring into private life. I read in a book once that a man should divide his life into three portions—the first portion for his childhood, the second for the administration of his worldly affairs, and the third for rest and remembrance of God. Your honor surely might well come home now and live comfortably.'

The Maulavi sáhib said: 'In the first place, the Chief would never let me go. And in the second place, there must be someone, at any rate, who could do the work in my place.'

'If your honor pleads that your strength is failing,' said Asghari, 'very likely the Chief will give in. And is not my dear brother fully competent to do the work?'

The Maulavi said: 'What does he know about the ways of the courts, and of the Darbár?'

Asghari said: 'Send for him to come here for a time, and let him be with you; he will pick up all that when he sees how it is done. Why, he is a learned Arabic scholar. There are Hindus who begin doing Kachahri work after reading two or three books in Persian.'

Asghari's notion approved itself to the Maulavi sáhib, and shortly after she arrived in Delhi he summoned Muhammad Aqil to join him. After some little time Muhammad Aqil took the whole of his father's work upon his own shoulders, and greatly pleased the Chief by his diligence. Then the Maulavi sáhib said to the Chief: 'Now, if this boy may remain here in the service of your highness, it might please your highness to set me at liberty.

"Not rarely the arbiters of homage
Set free the retainer in his old age".'[4]

The Chief was at heart a most liberal man. He allotted the Maulavi sáhib a pension of twenty rupees a month for his lifetime, and he appointed Muhammad Aqil as his successor on full pay.

[4]A quotation from the Gulistán of Saadi.

CHAPTER
XXVI

As soon as Asghari got back to Delhi, she resumed her plans for Mahmúda: Husnára was now at her old home on a visit from Jhajjar, and Jamálára had come from her father-in-law's house at the same time in order to meet her younger sister. You will remember that the whole of the Hakím's family were devoted to Asghari. As soon as they heard of her arrival, both sisters were in a hurry to call on her. All kinds of greetings went on. Jamálára said: 'Mistress, I cannot tell you how my heart was set upon meeting you. To be sure, Husnára is your pupil, but I owe you more than any of your pupils. It was you who restored my desolated home to me.'

Asghari said: 'What merit have I?'

'Come, now, mistress,' said Jamálára. 'At all events, I shall never forget your kindness as long as I live. But what can I do? You do not accept any service that we people can render you. Were it not for that, if we gave you our skins to make your shoes of, even then may be what is due to you would not be paid.'

'In the first place,' said Asghari, 'it was not so very much that I was able to do; but if by virtue of your princely nature your honor has regarded any act of mine with approval, well, Begam sáhib, God has placed your honor in a position of unlimited power. To make poor people like us happy will be no great task to you.'

Husnára said: 'Eh, mistress! what words are these from your lips?'

'Listen to me, sister Husnára,' said Asghari. 'The relations of mistress and pupil between us are all over now. They lasted only while you were at school. Now (God keep you!) you are a married woman. And here are you, noble from your very birth, and at present the crowning jewel of a noble family; and there is she, the daughter and daughter-in-law of princes. At this moment there is not one other family of higher standing than you in the city. If anyone should reach *your* gate, and be denied, surely it is his *fate* that would be at fault.'

Husnára said: 'Come, mistress dear; what is it?'

Asghari said: 'Sister, it is a very difficult matter. Promise me that you will not let me be disappointed, and then I will tell you.'

Husnára and Jamálára thought that she was going to ask for a place in their household for some one or other. Both of them said: 'By Heaven, mistress! for your sake we are ready heart and soul. It was our one great wish that you should make some request of us.'

Asghari said: 'It is a matter which seems great to me; but if you two ladies are both prepared to help me heartily, it is no very great thing after all.'

Both sisters replied: 'Mistress, God knows if it is anything we can do we will not spare ourselves in the least.'

When Asghari had thus secured a distinct promise from them, she said: 'The one object of my ambition is this: that you will accept Mahmúda into your family as a daughter of the house.'

On hearing this, both sisters kept silence. Other topics of conversation were broached. When the two were about to get up to go, Asghari caught hold of Husnára's veil with one hand, and of Jamálára's veil with the other, and said: 'I intend to take my fee now by main force. I swear by Heaven I will not let you go until my prayer is granted.'

Husnára said: 'Why, mistress, what power do you think we have in the matter? Arjumand is only a boy as yet. And, besides, in matters of this kind, while the parents are alive, how can sisters interfere?'

Asghari said: 'When they are grown up and married, sisters, too, become on a level with their mother. Besides, family alliances are never entered into without the approval of all the members. It is not possible that you will not be consulted.'

Husnára said: 'Up to this time there has been no question of an engagement anywhere that we know of.'

Asghari said: 'Perhaps you are not aware, then, that a letter of proposal was sent to Ulwi Khán's house. That was subsequently withdrawn.'

Jamálára said: 'If you have heard so, mistress, no doubt one was sent; but not a word was ever said to us about the matter. I wonder what there was amiss with Ulwi Khán? Heaven knows why the proposal should have been withdrawn.'

In this way the conversation again began to drift elsewhere. Asghari said: 'Ladies, my request is being left in the background. Be so good as to let me have an answer—"Yes" or "No".'

Jamálára said: 'My dear mistress, how *can* we take your part?'

Said Asghari: 'Wealth, good qualities, good looks, these are the three main things. As for wealth, there is none left to us poor people even to mention. As to good qualities, you, sister Husnára, know Mahmúda well; you and she were companions for two whole years. Come, tell us the truth now; are modesty, consideration for others, good manners, amiability, self-possession under all circumstances, every kind of accomplishment—reading, writing, needlework, cooking—I say, are all these things to be found in Mahmúda or not? That she is my sister-in-law and my pupil has nothing to do with it. No, the girl herself was created full of all good qualities by God. Is it not so? If I am telling falsehoods, do you speak, sister Husnára.'

'Mistress,' said Husnára, 'can anyone throw dust upon the moon? Mahmúda begam, such was the will of God, has not her equal in any of the great houses. My goodness! could any of them hold a candle to her?'

'And as to good looks,' continued Asghari, 'a nose, two ears, two eyes, such as people ordinarily have, Mahmúda has also. She, too, is of Adam's stock, and as good as others are. When she reaches maturity her beauty will be more developed.'

'Mistress,' exclaimed Jamálára, 'do you call Mahmúda begam a child of Adam? By Heaven! she is a child of the Houris. For my part, I have never seen a really good-looking girl in any big house. It is a case of "tall shop and tasteless viands". Here are we two sisters—I declare there are many slave girls handsomer than we are. And Mahmúda is "now the sun and now the moon". Where does one ever see a woman of her beauty?'

'In that case, sister,' said Asghari, 'what is there amiss in us except our poverty? You may think it "little mouth and big words" of me to say so, but not so many generations have passed since Ali Naqi Khán found mercy with God; and, after all, we as well as you, reckon him among our ancestors.'

Both sisters said: 'Mistress, you are the jewel of our family. Are you and we two? One race, one blood!'

'Then why this hesitation?' said Asghari. 'Make me happy by granting my request.'

Husnára said: 'All right, mistress; I will mention the matter to my mother this very day.'

Asghari said: 'It is not the mentioning; I can do that myself. What I want is that you should give me your hearty co-operation, and now that the proposal has been broached, that you will see it brought to a successful issue.'

Both sisters gave her their word, and said: 'Please God, mistress, it shall all be managed as you wish.'

This being settled, the two sisters took their leave for the time. The next day Asghari went herself to call on Sultána begam, and presented her with a kerchief of very fine shawl-work, worth 200 rupees, which she had brought from Siyálkot. Sultána begam said: 'Mistress, you quite put me to shame. I ought to be discharging my obligations to you, and not, on the contrary, to be taking presents from you.'

Asghari said: 'I had this kerchief made to order expressly for your honor, and I hope your honor will be pleased to accept it. For a whole year and a half I had it tied up in my bundle, hoping that I should one day come back to Delhi and lay it before your honor.'

Sultána begam said: 'I must take it, then for the good luck it will bring me; but, by Heaven, I do feel ashamed! I would your honor had only asked something of *me* once in a way, so that my soul might be rejoiced.'

Having got this encouragement, Asghari stood up with clasped hands, and made known her desire. Sultána begam said: 'Very good, mistress; but pray sit down, won't you?'

Asghari said: 'I will only sit down *now*, when I have obtained my wish.'

Sultána begam caught her by the arm, and made her sit down, and then said: 'To arrange the affairs of one's sons and one's daughters is no light matter. When people are buying a cup from the potter, worth the eighth of a farthing, they strike it to see how it rings before they take it. And *this* is a bargain, involving all that their whole lives are worth to them. One dare not conclude it without anxious thought, and much advice and deliberation. Your honor has mentioned this matter to me; now I will consult the boy's father, and my elder sister, and one or two other members of the family, and then, whatever seems best, we shall see. At present Arjumand is but a boy; what hurry is there for him to be married?'

Asghari said: 'I have made a venture of my hopes for beyond my merits, just as in Egypt there was an old woman who ventured to bid for the patriarch Joseph with nothing in her hand but a hank of the cotton she had spun. Like her, I possess nothing, save poverty and humility, to offer in the transaction. Your honor's good nature is now my only resource.'

Although Sultána begam did not say anything, it was evident from her demeanour that she was not displeased at the proposal. When Asghari took leave, she said to Jamálára and Husnára as she passed them: 'The successes of this matter is now in the hands of you two ladies.'

CHAPTER
XXVII

After Asghari had left both the sisters lauded Mahmúda to the
skies. Sultána was already half won over, but it happened that
Sháh Zamáni begam too had a daughter, Dildár Jahán, and
Sháh Zamáni had cherished the idea of betrothing her own daughter
to Arjumand. Luck was so far on their side that Sháh Zamáni had
never actually spoken to her sister on the subject up to that date. When
Asghari mooted the project of an engagement with Mahmúda, Sultána
begam sent to inquire of Sháh Zamáni begam what was her opinion in
the matter. Sháh Zamáni was greatly disconcerted when she heard about
it. Her endeavour now was to arrange so that the proposal for Mahmúda
should fall to the ground, and then she would secure a definite
engagement with Dildár Jahán: At the time she merely returned a verbal
message that she would think over the matter and send an answer.

Next day she presented herself at the house in person, and when
the conversation was brought round to this topic, she said: 'Sister,
where are *you*? and where is the Maulavi sáhib? What bond is there
between the earth and the sky? Who brought this message here?'

Sultána said: 'It was the mistress.'

Sháh Zamáni said: 'I shall go myself to the mistress at once.'
Accordingly she took Husnára with her, and went to see Asghari, and
said to her: 'Mistress, considering that you are a person of such great
intelligence, did it never even occur to you that family alliances are
usually made with people in one's own rank of life? The reason why
the note came back from Ulwi Khán's house was that they would not

accede to a gold bedstead. And what will you give to Mahmúda, I should like to know?'

Asghari said: 'Begam sáhib, I simply made a proposal on behalf of the girl's marriage. I left no message that there was any girl for sale. Although the code of morals in this city has greatly deteriorated, I have never yet heard of a betrothal being made a mercantile transaction. Pray, if a man gives his *daughter* away is he to make a profit out of her? There remains the question of rank, and certainly, if wealth be taken as the standard, it is manifestly the case that we are out of the reckoning. We have not even the fourth part of what Ulwi Khán has. But your honor is marrying a *boy*; what does the trousseau signify to you? When a *girl* is being given in marriage, her people may well be anxious, and wonder how their daughter will fare hereafter. Or, should the other side be poor, and reduced to supporting themselves by pawning the incoming bride's trousseau, I can understand such a family being anxious about it. But your honor is *taking* a daughter, not giving one, and in your honor's house there is everything provided of God's free gift. All that behoves your honor is to find a girl, and here is a girl brought up under your honor's own eyes; not a circumstance about her is concealed from your honor. And what there is good or bad in her nature your honor well knows.'

Sháh Zamáni said: 'What then? I still say that when betrothals are being made people look to equality.'

'I beg your pardon, Begam sáhib,' said Asghari, 'I forgot. We must not think of equality now. Those were the days of our equality when Ali Naqi Khán gave his own sister in marriage *into* this family, and now the very same family is not considered equal for a daughter to be taken from it! What, have maggots attacked this house? It lacks wealth, forsooth! But such proud boasting is not pleasing to God.'

Asghari had taken her up so briskly that Sháh Zamáni was at a loss for an answer. She said: 'Mistress, you are getting angry.'

Asghari said: 'Begam sáhib, is it in my power to be angry with you? I was in hopes that your honor would assist me in this matter, and not to find that you yourself are displeased at it.'

Sháh Zamáni said: 'Mistress, if I offend you I cannot help it, but the match is not an equal one.'

'As far as wealth goes,' said Asghari, 'our side is no match for yours. In birth we claim an equality. In accomplishments, please God! *your* side will not be adjudged equal to ours. What then? Your side fails in one point, and our side fails in one point. But a *bride* such as ours you may go, lamp in hand, over the whole world and search for but never find.'

'Mistress,' said Sháh Zamáni, 'why do you not invite proposals on behalf of Iqbálmand Khán's boy?'

Asghari said: 'I heard there were negotiations on foot in your honor's family, and so I never entertained the idea. Besides, what lack is there of proposals? There are plenty of boys for the girls, and plenty of girls for the boys. The way I reasoned was this: here is a combination of wealth and ability; the latter quality is suitable for rich people, and they confer a certain grace upon it; if a betrothal be arranged it will be good for either party. However, if your honor disapproves, why not have him betrothed to Dildár Jahán?'

'Dildára,' said Sháh Zamáni, 'is still a child, and I wish to marry her elsewhere. Marriage between relations is not altogether free from objection.'

When she had said this Sháh Zamáni took her departure, but Husnára did not get up to go. Her aunt even said: 'Come, child!' but Husnára besought her to go first, saying that it was many years since she had met the mistress, and she wanted to have a talk with her. When Sháh Zamáni had left the house Husnára said: 'Mistress my mother approves; it is *she* who is bent on spoiling the business. She may say what she likes to the contrary, but her real object is that the betrothal should be determined with Dildára.'

Asghari said: 'It is for Providence to decide now. After all, what does my opinion stand for against her? But, sister Husnára, it was not such a bad notion of mine. It seemed to me that the two exactly fitted each other. Think what a great house yours is, and only this *one* long-wished for son! Whatever there is of money and possessions all belongs to him. The mere keeping up of such a vast establishment demands great mental ability, and great tact too is necessary. Mahmúda comes of a poor family, but what of that? God keep her! Her courage and tact are such as befit princes. Suppose some girl with no tact came into your family, and brought cart-loads of trousseau with her, of what use would they be? She would find it difficult to manage her own wealth discreetly. How would she be able to rule your family? Mahmúda, so God has ordained, is capable of ruling a kingdom. Then, again, sister, one thing which ought to be considered is, for what purpose are alliances made? In this world we ought to extend our social intimacies as far as possible. If you have kept every fresh alliance that is made within the walls of your own house, what have your gained? Whenever one arranges a marriage it should be outside the family.'

'Mistress,' said Husnára, 'both my elder sister and I have spoken to our mother clearly on every point, and now I will go and tell her all you have just been mentioning as well. I am in good hopes that our side will win.'

And so Asghari, having fully coached her up in her part, allowed Husnára to take leave.

At the other house, when Sháh Zamáni came back, she said to Sultána: 'Sister, I have told the mistress plainly to her face that it is no match between your family and hers, and that it behoves people not to let such proposals come from their lips without thinking.' But Sháh Zamáni was in this strait, that she herself could not advocate her own daughter's engagement with her own mouth. In her heart this engagement was what Sháh Zamáni desired, but she was under the impression that the agreement would be settled by the gentlemen of the family. For the present she could only dilate on the objection to Mahmúda on the score of poverty. In the end Sultána begam retired apart from Sháh Zamáni, and took counsel with her own two daughters, when Husnára said: 'Mother, the real truth of the matter is that our good Aunt is designing to keep the betrothal for Dildára.'

Sultána said: 'Well, why not ask Arjumand himself about it—as if you were saying it in fun, you know.'

Jamálára called her brother, and said: 'How, brother! there is a discussion going on about your marriage. Have not *you* anything to say about it? Say on, would you like Dildár Jahán?'

Arjumand was too shy to say anything out loud before his mother, but by a gesture to his two sisters he expressed a denial. Jamálára and Husnára found a new argument in his refusal.

'Good looks, a good figure, good brains, and natural tact,' said Husnára; 'these things, sufficient even for a make weight against Mahmúda, you will not find in any girl. Of course, if you want a gold bedstead to be provided, that is a thing which is beyond the reach of poor people like them.'

'Sister,' said Sultána, 'the chief thing to look at is the girl. By God's grace we have no lack of anything in the house as it is. What do we want with a big trousseau?'

'Well, then,' said Jamálára, 'why hesitate? Proceed with the matter in God's name.'

'And although they are badly off,' said Husnára, 'the mistress is a woman of many expedients. What if she does not *talk* much about it? when the time comes she will do a great deal more than is expected of her.'

Sultána said: 'Very well, when your father comes home we will see what he thinks about it.'

When the junior Hakim sáhib came in, Jamálára and Husnára put Mahmúda's case before him just as pleaders in Kachahri plead the cause of their clients, with the result that he, too, approved of the betrothal with Mahmúda.

At once the two sisters rushed off, heedless of their dignity, to Asghari's house. Muhammad Kámil's mother, who was in absolute ignorance of all that was going on, called out to them: 'What is it, Begam sáhib? what makes you in such a hurry? You should hold up your skirts as you go.'

Husnára said: 'Nothing; we are only going to the mistress.'

The instant she saw Asghari Husnára cried out: 'My benison, mistress! my benison on you! And now see about giving me my reward.'

Asghari said: 'May God send His benison on all of you ladies! But as for a reward, with what face can I offer you anything? My prayers are all I have to give, and you know that I pray for you night and day.'

'That won't do, mistress,' said Husnára; 'I insist upon having my mouth sweetened by you today.'

'Very well,' said Asghari, 'but sit down; you shall have some sweetmeats.' Then she called Diyánat, and, taking out five rupees, gave them into her hand, and said: 'Go at once and fetch some of her best sweetmeats from the bellwoman's shop, and some lumps of delight from the corner of the Dariba, and some pearl-drops from Sháh Tára's lane, and almonds from the Chándni Chowk, and roasted dál from the Nil ká katra,[1] and whipt cream from the Khánam's bázár.'

Meanwhile she entertained them both with pawn, but it was not long before the basket of good things arrived. Asghari, Akbari, Husnára, and Jamálára ate heartily of them together, and what was over they sent into the schoolroom. When the two latter ladies were about to depart, Asghari said; 'Up to this moment I have not spoken a word of this to the dear mother. I will now go and mention it to her, and, please, God, the day after tomorrow is a good day, both of the month and of the week; the customary ceremonies shall then be performed.'

[1]Pronounce Neel ká kuttra; the meaning is 'Indigo mart,' but it is the name of a mohulla.

CHAPTER

XXVIII

The two ladies took their departure. Asghari said to her mother-in-law: 'Mother dear, have you devised any plan for Mahmúda?'

Her mother-in-law said: 'What plan can I devise? If only a message would *come* from somewhere! My thoughts don't go beyond one place. I shall marry Mahmúda to Muhammad Sálih.'

Asghari said: 'Where is Muhammad Sálih, and where is Mahmúda? Brother[1] Muhammad Sálih's age will not be much less than that of our own dear brother.'

Muhammad Kámil's mother said: 'Yes, Aqil is six months older than Muhammad Sálih; they were both born in the same year.'

'Well,' said Asghari, 'that is not much difference.'

Muhammad Kámil's mother said: 'We are barely on calling terms anywhere else.'

'I have thought of a plan,' said Asghari; 'if your honour approves, we will talk it over.'

Muhammad Kámil's mother asked: 'What is it?'

Asghari replied: 'With the son of the Hakim Fatih ullah Khán.'

Muhammad Kámil's mother said: 'My goodness, daughter, to live in a hut and dream of palaces! Where is the Hakím ji's family—with such wealth at their command nowadays that there is no one in the city to compare with them? and where are we poor creatures, who have not even a decent cottage to live in? Would it ever enter their heads to

[1] Really 'cousin'.

mate with us? To propose anything so indiscreet would only result in
our humiliation.'

Asghari said: 'If they are rich it is all for their own good. Do we,
God forbid it! depend at all on their bounty? If they are revelling in
puláos and *zardas*, we too are enamoured of our crushed grain and
pulse. In birth we do not yield a jot to them. And as for worth—good
heavens! there is more of that in our Mahmúda than ever fell to the
lot of their elders, I expect.'

'Sister,' said Muhammad Kámil's mother, 'worth before wealth stands
up with folded hands. If I could order the making of a gold bedstead,
then perhaps I might set about making such a proposal. No, my dear,
you may put that out of your thoughts altogether. Why, tell me, what
was there amiss in Ulwi Khán? After they had sent a note to his house
they recalled it. Sister, poor folk must rely on poor folk for their custom.'

Asghari said: 'Beauty alone is a fortune worth thousands. May any
evil eye be averted! I say they may search among all their kindred for
anyone better looking than our Mahmúda.'

'Sister,' said Muhammad Kámil's mother, 'you talk just like little
girls. Even beauty is taken into account only when it appears in someone
of equal rank. And then, is it a thing to say with one's own lips, "Our
daughter has a pretty face"? Besides, for my part, I don't understand
what curse there is upon beauty. I have seen very beautiful women
who were not valued at the price of their shoe-leather, and there are
hideous creatures who are cherished as the dearest of the dear.'

Said Asghari: 'Beauty too is a thing which people do well not to be
infatuated with; but it often happens that people whose outward appearance is lovely are inwardly vicious and aggressive in their tempers.
Being vain of their personal appearance, they take no pains to soften
the asperities of their inner nature, and so their evil temper beats
down the price of their beauty. You may compare them, say, with a
horse—faultless in colour, and clean-limbed, free from all blemishes,
and sound in every joint, but ill-broken and a biter, and given to
kicking as well, rearing whenever he is mounted, and falling over;
what *use* could a man make of such a brute though he bought him for
his beauty? But if, in addition to his outward attractiveness, he is well
trained, and clever in moving, and gentle withal, then he is an article

beyond all price. Like our Mahmúda, whose beauty of face and sweetness of disposition are only to be matched, praise God, the one by the other.'

Muhammad Kámil's mother said: 'For all that one must have something at least to give with her. Why, just now, one of the girls in your school was reading—

"'Yá makun bá fílbánán dosti,
Yá dare -afráz bar bálá-e píl,"[2]

which means, I take it, that either you should not cultivate the friendship of elephant riders, or, if you do, then you must raise the doorway of your house so that an elephant may go in and out. Where are we poor people to find the means of interchanging presents suitable to their rank? and what need have we to expose ourselves gratuitously to their laughter? Besides, say that the betrothal has actually been effected, and then the girl is looked down upon by all the people of her new home—"Your labour is lost, and your neighbours jibe".'

'Esteem and contempt,' said Asghari, 'are not determined by the bride's trousseau. The affection between husband and wife is something of a very different texture. Did Jamálára take a small trousseau with her? And yet it was not her luck to remain a single day in her husband's home. You need not go so far as that for an instance. My elder sister had a trousseau quite as good as mine, and yet why are they quarrelling every day? It is a question of each individual's tact and good temper.'

Muhammad Kámil's mother said: 'Yes, I admit that. True love between husband and wife does not depend on the trousseau. But all the relations and kinsfolk—will *they* be content without having their say? And suppose the boy takes no heed of their talk—what then? The mother-in-law and sisters-in-law can find opportunities to drop some ill-natured remark in the mere course of conversation. After all that does gall the feelings. A girl's parents have to lower their heads enough as it is, and to provide even a tolerable show of trousseau and presents is an extra calamity. No, sister, I don't see how *this* creeper is going to cover the trellis.'

[2]This is a couplet from the Gulistán of Saadi. The meaning is given in the following lines.

'We may leave the kinsfolk out of the question,' said Asghari; 'she won't have many of them sitting with her daily. True, the constant naggings of a mother-in-law and sisters-in-law are a terrible thing to face; but Husnára and Jamálára—is there any need to speak of taunts or sarcasms? They will be kissing the dust off Mahmúda's feet. The world has not gone dark all on a sudden. Or do you suppose they will thrust potsherds over their eyes directly she is married? Your honor can see for yourself how great an affection Husnára bears for Mahmúda. There is still Jamálára—God knows the secrets of her heart, but to all appearance she lays herself out to be kind to her whenever they are together. And, after all, I am here still alive; if they behave badly to Mahmúda, with what faces will they appear before me? And—one thing which counts for a hundred—I am perfectly certain of this: that mothers-in-law and sisters-in-law look which way the wind blows. If they see that the boy is in love with her, not one of them will dare to raise her eyebrows at Mahmúda.'

Muhammad Kámil's mother said: 'Still, I don't see what you are aiming at. Am I to have her wedded over a cup of sherbet?'

'No,' said Asghari, 'that is not my meaning. Besides, among the very poor, if even sherbet is not procurable, do they not arrange their sons' and daughters' affairs? To give and make others give is a custom of the world everywhere. People stretch their limbs as far as they can see their sheet. It is according to one's means; whatever can be managed is given and what can't be managed is not given. But there is no sense whatever in letting a family drift into bankruptcy through hankering after display. There is a girl named Sulma who reads in my school. After the Mutiny her father received a reward from the Government of ten thousand rupees. He had saved the life of some English lady. Ten thousand rupees to him was so large a sum that he might have lived respectably upon it for the rest of his days. He only had one son and one daughter, whose marriage expenses were still to be defrayed by him. But, yielding to his vanity, he not only cleared off the ten thousand rupees given to him by the Government, but spent several hundreds more which he raised by loan. At the time there were grand shouts of applause on all sides. Now, there is such scarcity in the house that they are at a loss even for a meal. I, too, received an invitation to the wedding.

It quite took my breath away to see the preparations. Indeed—perhaps Sulma's mother may have taken it ill of me—I said to her: "Sister, marrying a son or daughter is *eyes' delight and hearts' comfort,* and *where has the ghee gone? Into the khichri;* but still, one has need to take some compassion on one's own pot also". That was all I said at the time, and afterwards I had some compunction lest Sulma's sister might have thought that the school-mistress, with whom *she* had nothing whatever to do, was interfering unwarrantably.'

Muhammad Kámil's mother said: 'Yes, it is true. But we have to live in this world, bad luck to it! What can we do? Where can we go? A thing must be done, whether it ought to be or not. If people would not do as the world does, no one would be made a laughing-stock, and no one would be held up to admiration. At the lecture which Maulavi Isháq sáhib gave, I heard that in the old times the Arabs used to put their girls to death the instant they were born.'

'You need not go so far off as that, dear mother,' said Asghari. 'In our own country the Rájpúts were guilty of the same horrors. It has been put a stop to now since the English interfered, but still, there are rumours now and then of murders done secretly.'

Muhammad Kámil's mother said: 'What is one to think? It is revolting to the moral sense.'

Said Asghari: 'In poverty the moral sense does not count for much, and the majority of people in the world are very poor. If to be poor is a thing to be ashamed of, there are many in the world without shame. But, whether riches or poverty each has his own lot. And how *should* all men be of one pattern?'

'Heigh, heigh!' said the mother-in-law; 'for my part, I wish some law against excessive expenditure on weddings were made by the English Government. Then we should be rid of the bother.'

Asghari said: 'I saw in the papers that the English are going to take some measures. Indeed, all the chief men of this city were summoned to a meeting about it; and I heard that some limits to the expenditure had been fixed, the amount of the dowry being taken as the standard. But these are things which ought really to be done by *us* people. If *we* were all agreed, we might put a stop to every expense which is superfluous.'

Muhammad Kámil's mother said: 'But when you speak of expenses as superfluous, for those to whom God has given the means nothing is superfluous. I grant you, if a man has not a cowrie in his pocket, then everything for him is superfluous.'

Said Asghari: 'Let not your honor say so. The really necessary expenses at weddings are very small. An enormous amount of money goes in superfluities. Of course, in our family, we never think of having nautches and shows, and bands of music, and fire-works, or big-drums and kettle-drums; but among those who allow such things hundreds and thousands of rupees are sunk in them alone.'

Her mother-in-law said: 'The people who have nautches[3] and shows may look after their own affairs. But take people like us. What expenses that we incur are superfluous?'

Asghari: 'Are there not plenty? At the betrothal, the interchange of presents on festivals, the bridegroom's feast before the wedding, the henna, the bridegroom's procession, the bride's procession, the feast of the fourth day,[4] the bride's visits to her mother, and then the burdensome costumes, the jewelled ornaments—it is all superfluous.'

Mother-in-law: 'Why not say at once straight out that the wedding is superfluous to begin with?'

Asghari burst out laughing, and said: 'No, weddings are not superfluous. But all these accompanying formalities are mere useless padding.'

Mother-in-law: 'But it is not only the ceremonies. *You* call the dresses and jewellery superfluous.'

Asghari: 'As far as mere clothes and mere ornaments go, they are useful enough. But those heavily-embroidered costumes: I ask your honor, of what use are they? Why, my own are lying there simply rotting. I hate putting them on, worse luck! inside the house. Now and again I have worn them at weddings; or perhaps on the Eed they have been taken out for an hour or two. Except for that, there they are tied up in my bundle the whole year round. Putting them in the sun, when I have to do it, gives me a headache for the day which might

[3]Nautches are condemned by strict Musalmans.
[4]When the bride is taken in state to make her first call on her parents.

well be avoided. And if you should want to sell them, you don't get
the value of the material. People won't offer you the price even of the
trimmings. And it is just the same with the made-up jewellery. Did
your honor hear about the wedding of Maulavi Kifáyat ullah's
daughter? *That* is the kind of wedding I would choose.'

Mother-in-law: 'What Maulavi Kifáyat ullah is that?'

Asghari: 'The superintendent of girl-school teachers.'

Mother-in-law: 'He is not a resident of the City, I fancy.'

Asghari: 'No, his home is somewhere near Agra. But he has brought
his wife and children with him here. His daughter was betrothed within
the City, and his wife was bent on their going back to their own
home, and having the ceremony performed there; but the Maulavi
sáhib managed to win her over to his views. One day they summoned
a few of their intimate friends to the house. When the guests arrived,
they learnt it was the daughter's wedding-day; and shortly after, the
bridegroom's father made his appearance, bringing his boy with him.
The wedding vows were recited according to the Muhammadan ritual,
and with the blessing it was all over. Presents and trousseau were
conspicuous by their absence. But after the wedding the Maulavi sáhib
brought five hundred rupees in silver, and laid them before his daughter
and son-in-law, and said: "One minute, brother. See, the portion destined
for you by Providence out of my earnings was just this amount. If I had
wished, I might have entertained a lot of wedding guests out of it;
and, as the custom of the world is, I might have made up for you one or
two grand suits of clothing. But when I thought it over, it seemed to
me, under the circumstances, that it would be far better to give you the
money in cash. Do you now take the sum, and make use of it in any
way you like."'

After listening to this story, Muhammad Kámil's mother said: 'Yes,
away from home the Maulavi sáhib could do as he pleased. Who was
there to say him nay?'

Asghari: 'Who? Well, at any rate, there was his own wife. And must
we always wait to be away from home? It is courage we want. The
thing can be done well enough in the City if there is a man prepared to
do it. He has only to think of his own business, and let those chatter
who will.'

The mother-in-law: 'And is it this kind of dull, shabby wedding that you have designed for Mahmúda?'

Asghari: 'Most certainly I would not pay any attention to people's remarks. If I could have my own way, Mahmúda's wedding should be the counterpart of Maulavi Kifáyat ullah's daughter's. In fact, he *did* invite a few guests, and, in my opinion, even that was unnecessary.'

The mother-in-law: 'Nay, sister; for Heaven's sake, don't be so cruel. In my old age I have but this one child to give away in marriage. Shall I ever come back again from my grave to be at anyone's wedding?'

Asghari: 'But I don't say that anything of the kind is my intention. Only there is one thing that I am quite determined on, at least, in my own mind—that not a pice of debt shall be incurred, nor any property be mortgaged. Whatever money has been saved up, whatever has been put by expressly for her, and whatever, under Providence, may be in store for her at the time of the ceremony, *that*, I say, is quite enough.'

The mother-in-law: 'Extolled be the perfection of God! If only it could be so, what a good thing! But it depends on the other party's co-operation.'

Asghari: 'And suppose *they* should be willing?'

The mother-in-law: 'What nonsense, to think of their being willing! Why, he is their only son, granted after many prayers. Goodness knows what aspirations they have for him in their hearts. They will look about for some family equal in rank to their own, and then get him engaged, and satisfy all their ambitions.'

Asghari said: 'Ever since I came back from Siyálkot I have been engaged in arranging this matter. It is fixed all right on their side. Only just now Jamálára and Husnára came over here in a hurry to see me. The junior Hakím sáhib, too, has given his approval. Sháh Zamáni begam made all kinds of plans for the benefit of her own daughter, but by God's grace, not one was successful. And now there is no time to be lost. The day after tomorrow is a good day. From their side the sweetmeats will be sent, and then the *engagement* will be binding. We can see about the *marriage* afterwards.'

When Muhammad Kámil's mother heard this, she was lost in amazement. She said: 'It is an excellent match certainly, far beyond our merits. But it will be very difficult for us to make the preparations suitable to their rank.'

Said Asghari: 'God is the Causer of all causes. Since Mahmúda's lot has grappled with so high a family, God of His might will provide all that is necessary at the right time.'

Muhammad Kámil's mother said: 'Wait till your father-in-law comes home. I will see what he thinks about the sweetmeats.'

In a little while the Maulavi sáhib came in, and when he heard about the proposed betrothal he was highly delighted, and said: 'By all means, let the sweetmeats arrive.'

Asghari at once sent off a verbal message to Husnára. On the appointed day five maunds of sweetmeats and one hundred rupees arrived. One maund and a quarter of sweetmeats and a hundred and twenty-five rupees were despatched. From both sides good wishes and congratulations followed.

CHAPTER

XXIX

No sooner was the betrothal arranged than the Hakím sáhib began to manifest an impatience for the wedding. He sent a message to the Maulavi sáhib couched in these words: 'For a long time it has been my intention to make the pilgrimage to Mecca, and now I am delaying it solely for the completion of this rite. Life is uncertain. I should be glad if the marriage could take place in the month of Rajab.'

The Maulavi sáhib asked Asghari what he should do.

Asghari said: 'For the present you had better reply in the following terms: "The matter is engaging my earnest attention. I am doing my best to make the necessary arrangements. If I find it possible in so short a time to get together the few things I desire to give—I, too, have still before me that last obligation of a Muslim—the sooner the marriage can take place the better."'

In reply to this the Hakím sáhib sent another message to the effect that he had not sought the alliance with any expectation of dowry or trousseau, that all he begged of them was the bride, and that they need not trouble themselves about her appurtenances. To this they answered: 'Very well, the proposal for the wedding to take place in Rajab is agreeable to us also.' The twenty-seventh day of Rajab was fixed accordingly, and both parties began to make their arrangements.

At this juncture the Maulavi sáhib began to show signs of perturbation. At one minute he was assuring himself that he could raise a loan from Hazári Mal, and at the next he was debating in his mind whether he should sell the property known as the butter market, or only mortgage it. Asghari perceived that he was much disturbed in his mind. She asked him: 'What has your honor been projecting?'

The Maulavi sáhib replied: 'I wish I could tell you. Here is the date of the wedding coming close upon my head, and any means of procuring the money for it I cannot conceive. I asked Hazári Mal; even he put me off. Then I thought of parting with the butter market, but no purchaser comes forward.'

Asghari said: 'It will *never, never* do for your honor to borrow the money, and *please* do not sell any of your property either. There is nothing worse than being in debt. And it is easy enough to part with an estate, but very difficult to come by one.'

The Maulavi sáhib said: 'I am not to borrow, and I am not to sell. Do you suppose I am an alchymist? or that I know the secret of *the hidden hand?* Where is the money to come from?'

'Let us first take stock of what there is in the house,' said Asghari; 'most of the clothes have been ready some time; a few trimmings are still wanting, but among my robes there are one or two very heavily-embroidered ones—we can take some of the broideries off them, and they will make good the deficiency. The copper vessels are in the house—we don't want to buy any; as for the wooden articles, and all the little extras, I will give my own. They are lying doing nothing, and will only get spoilt, for I never use them. And then—well, your honor has *some* money in cash at all events?'

The Maulavi sáhib said: 'Only five hundred rupees.'

'Well,' said Asghari, 'that's plenty. At the time I started for Siyálkot the school fund amounted to four hundred rupees—that is in deposit. While I was away two hundred rupees more were made; half of that my elder sister is entitled to, but Mahmúda's share is one hundred; with that added to it, the school fund comes to five hundred. I wrote to Mahmúda's younger brother,[1] and asked him for three hundred; my brother-in-law has written to promise two hundred. You may say that we have fifteen hundred rupees in cash at this moment. Then there are the bracelets which were given to me at Husnára's wedding— what use are they to me? I had intended to put them upon Mahmúda

---

[1] *i.e.*, her own husband.

at her wedding, but afterwards I thought to myself it would not do for them to be returned to the same house from which they came, so I shall sell them. I sent them to the bázár through Tamásha Khánam, and Panna Mal made an offer of thirteen hundred rupees for them. If by Mahmúda's good luck we should find someone in need of such articles, please God, they will realize fifteen hundred. Another idea has come into my head. Your honor might well go to Lahore in order to fetch my brother-in-law, and when asking the Chief to grant him leave, might mention the reason for it. The Chief is very generous. It is quite possible he may help. This has been the custom of old with Hindustani princes. They have always helped their faithful adherents on such occasions.'

So it happened that Asghari sent her father-in-law to Lahore. When the Maulavi sáhib went to pay his respects to the Chief, the Chief asked him: 'Maulavi sáhib what has brought your honor here?'

The Maulavi sáhib then submitted his request: 'Your servant's daughter is about to be married, and his object in presenting himself is to solicit the boon of a month's leave for Muhammad Aqil. And your servant does not venture to ask that any member of your Highness's family should take a part in the ceremony, but if the *agent*, who is in Delhi, might grace the assemblage with his presence as your Highness's representative, it would produce in my behalf a great accession of dignity among my fellow-citizens.'

The Chief not only granted Muhammad Aqil's leave, but also defrayed the expense of the Maulavi sáhib's journey to Lahore and back, and he sent an order to the agent at Delhi to join the wedding party as his representative, and to make a present, as a guest's offering, of the sum of five hundred rupees. Here was a fine windfall realized without anyone's stirring a finger, and all through Asghari's advice. On the other hand, through Tamásha Khánam's good offices, the jewelled bracelets at last found their way to the Nawáb Hátim Zamáni begam, who was captivated by them at the first sight, and blindly made over two bags of a thousand rupees each to secure them. Thus from all sides there was a perfect rush of money. Under Asghari's management the very finest costumes were made ready, and a fourfold stock of jewellery. Such a wedding had not taken place in the Maulavi's family, at any rate, for many generations, and even the bridegroom's relations were astonished when they saw the bride's outfit. The articles of every kind were not only numerous but costly, and everything of the newest fashion. Two of the costumes, indeed, came from the bridegroom's people—one, for the wedding itself, of stiff brocade, and one of an embroidered pattern for the ceremony of the fourth day. As for the jewels—taking trousseau and presents together, there was no end to them—rings and pins for the nose, ornaments of several kinds for the forehead, earrings, plain and jewelled, of all sorts and sizes, necklaces and chains and pendants for the throat, armlets and bracelets of every device, rings for the fingers, anklets and rings for the feet and toes. The number of dresses, of different fabrics and textures, amounted altogether to fifty. There were two hundred metal dishes, and other articles of furniture upon the same scale. In short, the marriage ceremony was performed amidst the greatest display of pomp. Thus Mahmúda took leave of her old home, and in her father-in-law's house she received the title of Qamar Astáni begam.[2]

---

[2]'Lady Full Moon on the threshold.'

CHAPTER
XXX

✦✦✦

The Hakím Fatihullah Khán was a very sober, self-denying, and God-fearing man. For years he had cherished the desire of making the pilgrimage, but had been waiting to see Arjumand Khán well married. After the wedding he still remained for a time, bent upon watching the demeanour and behaviour of the bride. There was not much need for that in *her* case. Mahmúda had been polished upon Madam Asghari's lathe. There was not an uneven speck left on her surface. No matter what test he applied, the Hakím sáhib found his son's bride to be thoroughly educated, and of great natural ability, and full of tact. Like a melon, sweet of itself, and topped with the finest white sugar—to begin with, Mahmúda was good by her very nature, and she had benefited besides by Asghari's teaching and advice. What need to ask the result?

In short, the Hakim sáhib was satisfied beyond a doubt that Qamar Astáni would sustain the fortunes of his house to perfection. He forthwith commenced making preparations for his journey to Arabia in the most determined manner. He had bound himself to a pilgrimage; he now resolved to make it a migration. All the convertible property and cash which he possessed he put aside to take with him, but he had all the house property, shops, markets, warehouses, villages, and sarais registered in his son's name. This was not done without the remonstrances, as the custom is, of his own and his wife's relations; but the Hakím sáhib had god's message ringing in his ear, and was deaf to everything else. With the name of God on his lips he stood up to go upon his mission, and he bequeathed all his worldly possessions to his son and daughter-in-law.

Although Mahmúda was now a married woman, she regarded Asghari with greater respect and reverence, if possible, than before, and sought her advice upon the minutest points. It was now that Asghari found the opportunity of putting her natural ability to the proof. With a vast establishment, and business of the most important nature to be dealt with, she directed everything with such consummate ability that Arjumand Khán became, by her means (God preserve me from lying!), like one of the kings or wazirs of the age. No Chief's court could vie with his in Delhi—no, nor in the country for many miles round.

How much further am I to continue this narrative? Already so much has been written and yet, if you ask me truly, it is not one chitack out of a maund to what I could tell you. All this time Asghari has been living in a state of poverty. As the proverb says: 'Without clothes no woman can go bathing; what is she to *wring out*?'[1] But *now*, God keep her! power and affluence have fallen to her lot. The fullest scope and opportunity have been given her for the exercise of her administrative tact and ingenuity. The things which she achieved under these conditions—for all that she was a woman—will no doubt remain in the world as memorials of her to the last day; but unfortunately I have not the leisure to set them down in writing. Still, if there be anyone willing to accept instruction—who can listen to a word, and understand it, what has been already set down is not to be despised. All kinds of new ideas, and all sorts of lessons, are contained herein. We may call it a story for children, but in sooth it is a sermon for their elders. Before I bring the book to a conclusion, however, there is one other fact which I am bound to record, which is that, while she was still of tender years, Asghari became a mother. All this while I have not made any mention of her children. She had several, but as God willed, few of them survived their birth. The only one who lived to maturity was a son, Muhammad Akmal, who in later days was united in marriage

---

[1] A woman must have *two* suits of clothes to go bathing. The proverb is equivalent to our 'making bricks without straw.'

to Mahmúda's only daughter Mas-úda. This boy came after several other children, and, before he was born, one son named Muhammad Adil, and one daughter named Batúl had died.

There was no lack of pains taken in the children's bringing up. They were guarded alike from cold and from heat; the very times for feeding them were fixed, and the quantity of food given was by measure; the utmost care was taken to prevent their putting into their mouth anything unwholesome or fit to be thrown away; when their teeth began to come their gums were lanced lest the child should not win through the trouble of teething; at four years of age they were vaccinated to preserve them from small-pox; in a word, everything was done for them that human ingenuity could suggest, but in the face of God's decree the wisdom of the best of us avails nothing. Muhammad Adil was four years old when he died. He had an attack of indigestion. Some medicine was given to stop the purging. Fever supervened, and brought on inflammation of the brain. The mother had to give up her boy whom she had nursed so carefully through his infancy. While this sore was still fresh in her heart, Batúl, who had reached the age of seven, was taken ill. It was an outbreak of diarrhœa, so violent that, before its course could be checked, it carried away her life. All kinds of medicines were administered, but when does death yield to medicine? In the course of a single week the little girl gradually lost her strength, and faded away. The shock of *her* death fell upon Asghari very heavily. In the first place she was a girl, and then—whether because she was doomed to die early I do not know—she was so passionately attached to her mother that she would not be away from her for a moment. When her mother was at her devotions she would sit upon the prayer carpet; she would accompany her to bed, and get up with her at the same moment; even if it was her mother's medicine she must needs taste it; and such was her application to study that, at that early age, she had already begun the tenth portion of the vernacular translation of the Qur-án.

When Muhammad Adil died, the women about her commenced their efforts to sap Asghari's faith. One of them would say: 'He was begotten under some malign influence; you must get Mihr Ali Sháh the faqír to cure him;' and another: 'Someone overlooked his milk;

have a wave-offering placed on the cross-ways;' and another: 'It is the
rickets; have him exorcised by Ramazán Sháh;' and another: 'There is
something wrong with the house; get Mír Alím[2] to drive a nail into
the floor for you;' and another: 'You have been travelling hither and
thither; some night-hag has seized hold of him; go to Kachocha.'[3]
Twists and amulets, and spells and charms, and fetishes, from all quarters
of the world, were prescribed by this or that person. But, bravo, Asghari!
you never ceased to be thankful to God for His mercy; no, not even
when two of your children in succession were taken from you! To all
suggestions of the kind she returned the same answer: 'If it be God's
will He is at no loss, even so, to show me His bounty.'

---

[2]Pronounce Uleem.
[3]A village in Oudh where is the tomb of a very eminent Saint, named Saiyid
Ashraf Jahángír.

CHAPTER
XXXI

❧❧❧

W hen the news of Batúl's death reached him, Dúrandesh Khán sáhib was very greatly distressed, and it was with a troubled heart that he wrote to his daughter the following letter:

'To my dear child, Asghari Khánam, after my blessing,
'Be it known;

'I have only just learnt, by letter from Delhi, that Batúl has been taken from you. It would be impossible for me to pretend that this has not caused me pain, and yet my reason has not gone so far astray that I should give way to useless repining, like those who are without knowledge. My great trouble is for *you*. If this blow should seem to have fallen upon you with terrible severity, it is no wonder. But in every state of life it behoves God's servants to take counsel of their reason. God, in His mercy, has given us our reason for this very purpose—that we should get help from it, whether in sorrow or in joy. The facts of the world are such that we cannot avoid the necessity of pondering over them, and this kind of meditation is not devoid of profit. This earth and sky, the mountains and forests, and rivers, men, and beasts, and trees—all the thousands and thousands of different things that are in the world, they constitute one vast machine of which the world is the habitation. The sun's issuing in the daytime with steadfast regularity, and afterwards the coming on of night, and the gleaming of the moon and of the stars; the summer heat at one time,

the winter at another, and the rains at another, and through the influence
of rain the production of fruits and flowers of many forms and many
colours—every detail of the universe is sufficient by itself to occupy a
man's thoughts for years. And to any human being his own condition
is no small subject for meditation. How a man is born, and how he is
nurtured and grows, and how there pass over him the different stages
of boyhood and manhood and old age, and how at last he sets forth
upon a journey *beyond* this world—*that*, indeed, is a deep and difficult
theme to entertain. The whole of this vast machinery has been set in
motion by God for some good purpose, and will continue so to be in
motion for as long as He wills. This world is only some seven or eight
thousand years old, and now its time is but short, for the resurrection
is at hand, and all that we see around us is hastening to destruction. It
has been proved by statistics that three and a half thousand human
beings die in every hour—that is to say, about one person at every
moment—and an equal number, no doubt, are being born. You may
easily reckon that in a single month many hundreds of thousands of
persons are dying, and are being born into the world, and then consider
that this has been going on uninterruptedly for seven thousand years,
which means that an incalculable number of persons have already died
in this world up to the present. What we call "death", therefore, is
something normal and inevitable. The greatest and mightiest kings,
the most famous scholars, the cleverest physicians, even great prophets—
men who had power to raise the dead to life—could not escape from
death themselves. Whoever is born into this world must one day die:
such is God's imperative decree. So that if on any particular day this
decree be put in force against ourselves, or against someone near and
dear to us, we have no excuse for complaint or lamentation. These
remarks are not mere platitudes. Think over them well, and when you
realize what the true meaning of death is, I am certain you will consider
as I do—that to grieve for the death of anyone is futile and unprofitable.

'Our grief at a person's death depends upon the strength of our
attachment for him. If I hear that the Emperor of China is dead, the
news does not affect me in the least, for the simple reason that there
was never any tie between him and myself. And if anyone outside the
family should die, even in the mohulla, unless I had some special interest

in him, it would cause me very little concern. It is only when we are connected with the person by some tie that we really grieve at his death, and the stronger the tie the greater the grief. If a female cousin of my maternal grandmother's sister-in-law's sister's daughter-in-law die it is nothing to me; the relationship is too distant. In fact, it is not merely relationship that has to be considered, for grief makes its presence equally felt in the case of friendship or intimacy. Thus one needs to settle which person it is in the world for whom we have the greatest attachment, and for that there is no fixed rule. We may imagine the closest relationship, and constant quarrels and disagreements. Such relations are out of the reckoning. And, on the other hand, an outsider, with whom there is no connection by blood or marriage, but strong affection and a community of interest, is often valued more than relations. But we may take it that each individual, according to his bent, has some special attachment of his own. Now, all these ties of the world's making are based upon considerations of self-interest and profit. For if my nearest relation should set himself to oppose my interest, it is certain he would lose my affection; and if an outsider should bestir himself for my benefit, it is certain he would be esteemed as dear as any relation. And it does not necessarily follow that the benefits which create ties of this kind should be such as can be estimated in rupees and pice, although, no doubt, this is frequently the case. Sometimes a tie is created by the mere expectation of some advantage. I have many friends who do not give me anything, but the mere prospect of their being willing to help me, in the event of my requiring their assistance, becomes a reason for my attaching myself to them. I might pursue this topic to any length, and it is one which might be discussed at great length with advantage, but it was my sole intention in this letter to deal with the subject of parental ties, and if I have leisure, please God, I will some day write a book about worldly attachments and send it you.

'The ties which bind parents to their children are common to all beings. No father or mother is exempt from them, not even in the brute creation. From this it is evident that these ties are not based merely upon self-interest and advantage. Nay, rather, it is in harmony with the scheme which the All-wise Ruler of the universe has ordained for the government of the world that parents *must needs* have a love for their own offspring. For several years children depend wholly upon others for their nourishment and support. In order that they should be properly nourished, God has planted in the parents such a love for their offspring that they are constrained by its promptings to cherish them, and bring them up, until such time as they are big enough and old enough to fare for themselves in the world. That is to say, parents, are the body-servants of their children for the purpose of attending to their wants. Yes, *to bring their offspring up properly*, that is the sole tie which has been conferred upon parents by God's ordinance. If we go beyond this, all those worries, such as the longing to have children, and when there are none the recourse to doctors and medicines, to charms and amulets, or religious exercises; or, supposing there are children, the anxiety that they should be boys and not girls, or, whichever they are, that they should be long-lived—all these are merely the flashes of *human* desire. And now we have to consider *why* this hankering for offspring, which man has created for himself in excess of God's will, should exist, and what is the cause of it. Undoubtedly it is due to motives of self-interest and advantage, but these motives are not all of the same kind. Some people think that their posterity will hand their name down to future generations, some look forward to being assisted by their children in their own old age, and some cherish the notion that after their death their children will inherit their estate, and manage their property. We have only to examine these fancies to perceive how absurd and erroneous they are.

'What is meant by transmitting one's name to posterity? Simply this: When people see a man, they are to know that he is the son of *So-and-so*, or the grandson of *So-and-so*. In the first place, when I myself am no longer in the world, what is it to me whether anyone knows my name or not? But, further, it is a question how far one's name is handed down. Ask anyone the names of his ancestors. Perhaps in most cases he will be able to tell you as far back as his grandfather; beyond that, even their own posterity cannot tell you what mighty man was their great-grandfather, or their great-great-grandfather. Besides, what object have they in digging up the bones of their dead ones? Thus, if we assume that the name is transmitted, it is only for a generation or two at the most, and then who cares? But it is a mere conceit to grant even that. Here am I, living in the Hills for the last ten years. I know thousands of men here, and thousands know me, but I doubt if any of them know who my father was; nor am I acquainted with their fathers, nor does the necessity for giving or seeking information on the subject ever arise.

'The second reason for parents' desiring offspring is the advantage which they look forward to in being tended by their children in their old age. This assumption, also, is the merest folly. What assurance have I that I shall be alive when my children are grown up? or that they will survive until old age comes upon me? And if this coincidence be granted, even then the children's being of any help to their parents is altogether problematical. I do not find so many instances in these days of children bent on showing respect to their parents, or anxious to render them any service. Nay, so far from respect and service, most children nowadays cause their parents annoyance and discomfort. People long to have children, but when they come they are a source of sorrow to their parents from first to last. Think of the plague it is to rear them when they are infants. At one time their eyes give trouble; then it is a pain in the chest; another time they are teething; another time they catch the small-pox. After many woes they grow out of that stage; then there comes the anxiety of clothing and feeding them. No matter what a man's circumstances are—he may be in service or out of employ—but whether he has money in his purse or not he must give to them, wherever it comes from. If the father and mother go without their meals, so they may; but the children, even if they cannot buy their own sweeties, must have a halfpenny-worth of parched gram every day.[1] Whenever the Eed comes round, or the Baqar Eed, or there is a fair, or a festival, 'Now, brother, some new clothes,' 'Four halfpence to buy sweeties with—'if you get off with *that* you are lucky. And *now* the parents desire that their boy should be learning something, and go to school; and the boy is such a cub that he runs miles away from the very mention of books, and nothing will induce him to go to school until four of his schoolmates drag him there by

[1] *i.e.*, independently of their regular meals.

force; and when he has got there, if the master loses sight of him for a moment, he will be out on the crossways, or playing tipcat by the edge of the canal, or throwing up dust in the streets. When he grows a little older, he begins to set his parents at defiance; he makes friends with idle and dissolute youths; he does not scruple to go to nautches, nor shrink from evil company; he wanders about bringing disgrace on the family name. And some there are who in this way go utterly to the bad, and become thieves, or gamblers, or drunkards. Then, when the daughters are old enough to be married, you go through the list of all the houses in the city without being able to find a suitable betrothal. The professional match-maker is worn off her legs. Your acquaintances have given up the job in despair. You have spoken to the heads of all the branches of your family one by one, but no one will help you. Your very life becomes a burden. The wretched mother goes about paying vows to the saints. She stands and listens for some 'omen of the voice.'[2] She celebrates a doll's marriage. All the five times she ends her prayers with the cry, 'O God, from Thy hidden store send someone!' And when, after many tears, the betrothal has at last been arranged, it is with such a family that here is the poor mother without a tag of silver to her name, and the parents on the other side insist on ear-rings of the most elaborate pattern. By hook and by crook, after pawning all you are worth, the marriage becomes an accomplished fact. But, 'The guests are not fain for the fine bird you've slain.' The trousseau goes the round of the family, and is scoffed at by everyone. 'Tchut!' says the bridegroom's mother. 'Fancy their giving things like these! Why *will* people *have* daughters if they are so poor?' There is not a single article which they approve of. One sarcastic remark leads up to another. And when Mr. *your son-in-law* honours your house with a visit, there is no end to his arrogance. Until he has seen that his father-in-law has put his shoes[3] where he can easily step into them again he won't even wash his hands; you need not mention dinner. Then perhaps before the ceremony of the fourth day is over, the bride and bridegroom are ready to shoe-beat each other. You have given

---

[2]*i.e.*, some chance word or phrase not intended for the listener, but striking a chord in his inner consciousness.

[3]The shoes are taken off before people enter a room that has a carpet.

away your daughter in good faith, and secured for her nothing in return but a quarrel. Nor is this a grief which passes in a single day. No, a wheel of misfortune has been set going for the rest of your life. As soon as such a daughter has children, her mother becomes an unpurchased slave, a nurse without wages. She has spent all her days moiling and toiling to bring up her own children, and now, when she hoped that fate had in store for her a year or two of the rest she had prayed for, she has to undertake the nursing of her daughter's little ones.

'And suppose it is your *son* who has married and brought home his bride—the discord, the quarrels, which she brings into the house by the bushel! She does not value her mother-in-law so high as her shoe-leather. She is always driving her sisters-in-law to the verge of despair. She has no reserve before her elder brother-in-law, and no respect for her father-in-law. A woman—and she knocks their turbans off the heads of the men. God take them under His protection! And what think you of the undutiful son? When his wife has created all this disturbance in the house, the renegade takes her part, and actually quarrels with his own parents! Until at last the wretched father and mother are driven out of their house, and forced to hire a lodging for themselves elsewhere. *That* is the goal to which the young folk of this age bring their parents, and few indeed are they to whom their children are a source of comfort. When in our folly we are importunate to have children, we know not what we are doing. It is as though we invited trouble and calamity in our prayers.

'There is only one more theory to dispose of—viz., that there ought to be someone to inherit the property, and *therefore* a man must wish for children. How perverted, and senseless, and weak, and flimsy an argument this is you can see at a glance. When a man himself has bid adieu to the world, what does it matter whether his estate is taken charge of by sons, or whether it reverts to Government as unclaimed property? The riches of this world are of no value in the world to come, if we except, indeed, what a man may give himself "in the way of God"[4] before he dies, or what may be given for him "in the way of God"

---

[4]*i.e.*, to widows and orphans and the very poor.

after his death. But if I have not employed my riches in this way personally, and have left so important a duty to be discharged by my heirs, there is no greater fool in the world than I. Children who obtain gratis all that their parents have heaped together are most unlikely to be frugal in their expenditure of it. A man knows the value of that money which he has earned by the strength of his arm and the sweat of his brow; and to the money which comes to anyone as a free gift you may well apply the proverb, *Wealth without toil, and a heart without compassion.* No doubt the children will scatter their inheritance freely enough upon nautches and shows, and gadding about, and sight-seeing; but when it comes to having a prayer offered in their father's name over a small heap, even of millet, for distribution to the poor, *that* is quite out of the question. Are there not hundreds and thousands of instances in the world of people accumulating riches all their life long by meannesses and stinginess, and the instant their heirs have got hold of it, so great has been their extravagance that the savings of a father's lifetime have disappeared in a few days?

'Oh the farce of it! and *who* squandered! and *who* was he who saved!'[5]

'From this statement of the case it will be apparent to you that all that exuberance of sentiment which men of their own perversity have developed in excess of the parental tie works infinite harm to themselves. Our orders are to observe this tie so far: as long as children are in need of our assistance, we must devote ourselves to their welfare; but in doing this we are not to give place in our hearts to the hope that, when they are grown up, they will *compensate* us for our efforts by their devotion to us.[6] To entertain this hope is the height of folly.

[5]The original of this line occurs in a poem of Háfiz, but is commonly quoted without reference to its context.

[6]The tendency of human nature to demand compensations is the theme of a quatrain by Háli (India's greatest living poet), of which the following is an almost word for word translation:

'There is in the *self* of man, by nature, this disease,
  That he seeks a compensation for each effort he makes.
  Deeds, which I had done purely for God's sake,—when I looked,
  There was hidden in *them* even some selfish aim.'

Rather, we ought to consider that God, who is our Supreme Master, has imposed upon us this *duty* of attending to their needs, and that, in bringing up our children properly, we are performing His behest. This orchard is God's, and we are the gardeners of the orchard appointed by Him. If the Lord of the orchard give an order to prune, or to cut down any tree, what right has the gardener to say, 'I have tended this tree with great labour, why should it be cut down?' or 'Why should its branches be cut off?' All the ties which exist in the world have but one purpose—that men should be *of use* the one to the other. We have been sent into this world for some good reason for a few days only, and while we are here, God has made us fathers, or sons, or brothers, to other men, in order that we should help others, and that others should help us, and that we should serve the full period of lifetime allotted to us amidst goodwill and kindliness. This world is not our home. We shall have to go and *live* elsewhere. Nor is anyone here our own, nor do we belong to anyone here. If we are fathers, it is but for a little while; and if we are sons, that, too, is but for a little while. If we see anyone dying, what subject is it for lamentation? We might lament in one case—if *we* were to be left here for ever. But we ourselves have the same journey before us. And we know not at what hour the summons may come, and the day of our departure be fixed. And, what is more awful still, we know that death is not merely the flitting of the life out of the body, as though the soul had moved from one dwelling into another. No, but when man arrives at that bourn, he will have to give an account of every little thing that he has done. The tongue must answer for every lie, and slander, and oath, and foul saying, and foolish word. The eye will receive its retribution for every glance of envy or covetousness. The ear will suffer chastisement for having listened to calumny, or to seductive strains. If the hand have been stretched out in violence or theft, it will be cut off. If the foot have wandered from the right way, it will be made fast in the stocks. A time of great peril will it be. God alone, of His mercy, send our boat across the flood! *then* may we reach the shore. If there be anyone who has found peace for himself from thoughts like these, *he* may have leisure to grieve for the death, or rejoice at the birth, of his fellows. But who is there in this world who has already attained to such security about his future? Oh, Asghari! take heed to yourself, and make preparation for that day in which nothing of your own, except your own deeds will avail you. And pray that the Lord of all things, through the favour of His loving servant Muhammad (on him be the blessing of God, and His peace!) may grant to all of us in the end a happy issue. And now my blessing upon you!

'The sinner,
'Durandesh Khán.'

RECOMMENDATIONS

Recommendation by the Nobly Descended, Most Learned of the Learned, M. Kempson, Ṣāḥib Bahādur, Director of Instruction, North West Provinces

The arrival of this book brought me much happiness, because this book is the composition of a worthy and highly accomplished servant of the Government. The author is among those three Hindustani persons whom some years ago Sir George Edmonston, the previous lieutenant Governor, selected to translate the Indian Penal Code into the Urdu language. Thus through the speed of this service he obtained a robe of honor, and since that time has been employed in high positions in the Revenue Department. This book is extremely interesting, and is suited to the circumstances of the people of this country. Up to now, no book of this type has existed, and from the point of view of style and manner of expression it is a very good example of the Urdu language. This book is equal to the recently published letters of Mirzā Naushah Dihlavī whose pen name is 'Ghālib', and in truth it resembles the Urdu of *Alf Lailah* and Badr ud-Dīn Ḳhān Dihlavī's *Bostān-e- khiyāl*.

Naẓīr Aḥmad's work is fit for everyday reading, and is popularly understandable, and its meaning is clear and worthy of being put into practice. In it there are no romantic themes and delicate thoughts such as the writers of this country consider to be their path to fame. And I hope that many more people too will imitate this writer.

This book has clearly been written for the benefit of women, and in it the imaginary story of a well-bred [*sharīf*] family of the Muslim community has been told. This whole story has been told in the colloquial language of those of good family, for *this* is the true Urdu of this country, not the kind filled with great big words and colourful themes for the sake of display. In truth, just such incidents have been written down as constantly confront every single woman in her in-laws' house. And the ways and manners of the women's quarters have been narrated in such a way that if a European reads the book, to some extent he will get a first impression of the daily circumstances of the women of this country. Women's language, and their affections and hatreds, and their loving care of children, and their influence over the tasks of housekeeping, and their barbarous ignorance and envy and trickery—in the book, he makes all this very plain, and not a word is to be found exaggerated because of style.

It's clear that the writer has narrated the true reality, and the story's advice emerges from the very soul of the story. The intellectual value of parables is well-known and well accepted, but in this book he has not sought to express them, and the thoughts that he has written down here and there show simplicity and straightforwardness. People's words that are mentioned in this appear to the reader's eyes as though they are being copied from life. As far as I know, before this no Hindustani writer has presented the true reality through conversation and dialogue in such a way, without loquacity and shows of temperament. When this book becomes famous, hundreds of people [*ādmī*] will read it with enthusiasm, and it's impossible that it won't be beneficial for the education of women.[1]

⁂

Recommendation by the Gracious Lord of Exalted Titles, Navāb Sir William Muir Ṣāḥib Bahādur, K.C.S.I., Lieutenant Governor, North West Provinces

His Lordship Navāb the Lieutenant Governor Bahādur inspected the book *Mirāt ul-'Arūs* and was very much pleased. This book is of such a

---

[1]This recommendation appears in Naẓīr Aḥmad, *Mirāt ul-'Arūs*, pp. 4–6.

rank that in the opinion of the admired Navāb, no other book in Urdu is its equal. And as for the praise that the Director Ṣāḥib Bahādur has written—in truth, the book is worthy of it. The events are exactly like personal experience, the language is clear and without ornamentation, and the incidents of the domestic life of the Hindustanis have been narrated most straightforwardly, just as they are in reality. Every single person whose speech is mentioned in it has an individual personality that shows itself quite distinctly. And for this reason, here and there, without artificiality, it can be found to affect the heart and create a sympathetic mood. And from every incident there emerges some counsel about the cultivation of morality or the refinement of social behaviour.

This book shows very well that in Hindustan women who keep purdah have considerable influence in the affairs of the household; and when the effect of education falls on intelligence and virtue, that influence can be the cause of extremely desirable results. And the thought never even enters the mind that any well-bred Hindustani man would read this book and the advantages—which are countless—of the education of women would not be engraved on his heart.

Moreover, a remarkable quality of this book is that it's very suitable for reading by the women of Hindustan. It is impossible that it wouldn't appeal to them, and wouldn't improve their wisdom and understanding. And no well-bred Hindustani man should hesitate to cause this book to be read in his family; rather, he should be confident that it will be read with enthusiasm and with intellectual benefit as well. In the whole book there's no theme which is not pure and refined, and which does not teach some rule or principle that is, especially from a Muslim point of view, free of fault and full of virtue. Muḥammad Naẕīr Aḥmad deserves high praise for having devised a new path toward virtue, and for having created, in plain speech, a beneficial and interesting example for others.

His Lordship Navāb the Lieutenant Governor Bahādur is confident that many people will quickly imitate this style. His Lordship Navāb the Lieutenant Governor Bahādur is particularly pleased to award to Muḥammad Naẕīr Aḥmad the full prize of one thousand rupees. In addition, to show his esteem, from his own private purse he will bestow on him a watch on which suitable words will be engraved. And he hopes that this award may be bestowed publicly on Muḥammad Naẓīr Aḥmad in a durbar at a place convenient to him—that is, perhaps in Etawah, when His Excellency's camp passes through that city. It will be ordered that for the Government's part two thousand lithographed copies at once be printed in an extremely attractive style, and Muḥammad Naẓīr Aḥmad has permission to retain the copyright to this book and make suitable arrangements on his own part for printing it.

It is believed that this book will acquire great fame. Although in the eyes of readers of local languages its simple and plain style may at first seem unadorned and too innovative, His Lordship Navāb the Lieutenant Governor Bahādur considers it proper to recommend to the gentlemen of the examination board that this book is worthy to be included on examinations. That is, in comparison to the common, customary, insipid tales of this country—for they are often objectionable as well.

From the extremely fine themes of this book, the readers will obtain not only the benefit of acquaintance with plain and eloquent everyday language, but also great familiarity with household arrangements. And people who have to work with others in order to set up a household will assuredly find it effective in dealing with convoluted matters.[1]

[1]This recommendation appears in Naẓīr Aḥmad, *Mirāt ul-'Arūs*, pp. 7–9.

AFTERWORD:
THE FIRST URDU BESTSELLER

A story of two sisters named Great (Akbarī) and Small (Aṣg̱harī)—
right from the start we're in didactic territory. Don't we already
sense that the younger sister will be the heroine? If there were
a sister named Middle too, the fairy-tale likeness would be complete.

The Bride's Mirror (Mirāt ul-ʿArūs) may or may not have been the
first Urdu novel, but it was certainly the first Urdu bestseller. Released
in 1869, within twenty years it had appeared in editions totalling over
100,000 copies; it had also, its publisher claimed, been translated into
Bengali, Braj, Kashmiri, Punjabi, and Gujarati.[1] It had been adopted
for almost every Urdu syllabus, and in fact has not been out of print in
Urdu from that day to this. In 1903 an English translation was published
in London by G.E. Ward; it is this translation that is reproduced in the
present volume. Ward was such a careful student of the work that he
had already, four years earlier, laboriously produced and published an
entire roman-script version of the text, with partial annotation and a
complete cumulative glossary.[2]

The Bride's Mirror was its author's first literary success. Naẕīr Aḥmad
(1831–1912) came from a family with a distinguished religious ancestry.[3]
His father, a teacher in a small town near Bijnore, taught the boy Persian
and Arabic, and in 1842 took him to study with Maulvi ʿAbd ul-Ḵẖāliq

---

[1]Russell, The Pursuit of Urdu Literature, p. 265, note 28.
[2]Ward, The Bride's Mirror, 1903 and 1899.
[3]This account of Naẕīr Aḥmad's life draws generally on Russell, The Pursuit
of Urdu Literature, pp. 112–20.

at the Aurangabadi Mosque in Delhi. In 1846, the boy had the opportunity to enroll at Delhi College, and studied there till 1853; he chose its Urdu section, he later said, because his father had told him 'he would rather see me die than learn English.'[4] During this period he also discreetly arranged his own marriage, to Maulvī 'Abd ul-Khāliq's granddaughter. Though he passed it off as the usual parentally-arranged marriage, many years later he urged his son in a letter to plan his own marriage, as he himself had done.

In 1854 he joined the British colonial administration, and his career prospered: in 1856 he became a deputy inspector of schools in Kanpur, and at the end of 1857 he was appointed to a similar deputy inspector-ship in Allahabad. On the advice of a friend, he took six months' leave and spent the time acquiring a working knowledge of English. In 1859–60 he began translating the Income Tax Law into English, and followed it with the Indian Penal Code, a project completed in 1861. In 1863 he was rewarded with the post of Deputy Collector in the Revenue Ser-vice (hence his conventional title of 'Deputy' Naẕīr Aḥmad), and was posted in various cities. Around 1865 or 1866 he started to write school textbooks in Urdu.

Then in 1868, the government of the Northwest Frontier Provinces began to offer prizes for books judged suitable for educational use: the conditions were 'that the book shall subserve some useful purpose, either of instruction, entertainment, or mental discipline; that it shall be written in one or other of the current dialects, Oordoo or Hindee, and that there shall be excellence both in the style and treatment.' Only one further stipulation was made: 'Books suitable for the women of India will be especially acceptable, and well rewarded.'[5]

These prizes continued to be offered for some years, and *The Bride's Mirror* was awarded one in 1870. The work was so esteemed that its author received not only the maximum prize of Rs. 1,000, but also a watch as a personal token from the lieutenant governor; in addition, the government purchased 2,000 copies of the book and recommended its inclusion in school syllabi.[6] Naẕīr Aḥmad claimed that he had

[4]Gupta, *Delhi Between Two Empires*, p. 7.
[5]Naim, 'Prize-Winning *Adab*', pp. 292–93.
[6]Naim, 'Prize-Winning *Adab*', p. 300.

written the story for the pleasure of his own daughters, after which it became such a neighborhood favorite that 'as a jewel of great price' it formed a part of his oldest daughter's dowry [2][7]; only by chance, he maintained, had his British superior Matthew Kempson seen it and caused it to be entered for the prize. This account, however, like some other famous anecdotes, seems to be a product of his pleasure in 'telling tales' and 'adding drama to the events of his life.'[8]

In 1872 the author produced what he called the 'second part' of his tale, Banāt un-Na'sh (The Daughters of the Bier, a name for the constellation Ursa Major), which won a prize of Rs. 500. He continued to write and translate educational and practical works, and in 1874 he once again won the grand prize of Rs. 1,000 with Taubat un-Naṣūḥ (The Repentance of Naṣūḥ). This work so pleased Matthew Kempson, the Director of Public Instruction, that he personally translated it into English.[9]

Through the good offices of the great social reformer Sir Sayyid Aḥmad Khān (1817–98), in 1877 Naẕīr Aḥmad was offered a well-paid position in the administration of the princely state of Hyderabad. He remained there until 1884, when court politics caused him to resign and return to Delhi, where he lived for the rest of his life. During his years in Hyderabad, though he wrote almost nothing, he is said to have learned Telugu and memorized all of the Quran. Back in Delhi, he composed four more tales: Fasānah-e Mubtalā (1885), Ibn ul-Vaqt (1888), and the much less famous Ayyāmah (1891) and Rūyā-e Ṣādiqah (1892).

At this point he ceased to write fiction, and began to participate in Sir Sayyid Ahmad Khān's various political activities; he developed into a popular, effective, humorous public speaker. Eventually he turned his attention toward religious reform, and composed a number of thoughtful, candid, liberal-minded essays. He died of a stroke in 1912. But his influence lived on, and not just through his writings: his family maintained a tradition of female literacy, and he influenced the literary

[7]This and all other bracketed page numbers refer to Ward's translation, as contained in the present volume.

[8]Ṣiddīqī, p. 47, quoted in Russell, The Pursuit of Urdu Literature, p. 115.

[9]Naim, 'Prize-Winning Adab', pp. 300–01. See also Kempson, The Repentance of Nussooh.

career of one of his nephews by marriage, Rāshid ul-Khairī (1868–1936), who not only became one of the most prolific and popular Urdu novelists of his time, but also in 1908 founded *'Iṣmat* (Honor), the earliest Urdu literary magazine for women.[10]

Naẓīr Aḥmad described his first three tales as forming 'a syllabus for the instruction of women': *The Bride's Mirror* was for teaching household arts, *The Daughters of the Bier* for teaching useful facts, and *The Repentance of Naṣūḥ* for teaching piety. There is certainly, as C.M. Naim notes, 'some internal evidence to suggest that the series was planned'—or at least, that a series was planned, though it may have evolved in the course of its writing. Nevertheless, the quality and reputation of the three tales differ markedly. The second tale is much the weakest—it consists largely of an account of the school run by Asghari—while the first and third are the author's most famous works, with most critics preferring the third. *The Bride's Mirror*, the one that started it all, became such a popular favorite that in the days of its greatest fame it was, like a fairy tale, 'simply known as the story of Akbari and Asghari.'[11]

The chorus of praise that greeted *The Bride's Mirror* was almost universal—but not quite. The influential religious scholar Maulānā Ashraf 'Alī Thānvī (1864–1943) took a dim view of the work. His own famous didactic work *Bihishtī Zevar* (*Heavenly Jewels*) was commonly given to brides, since it contained encyclopedic advice for every part of their domestic and religious lives. And in his list of harmful books that should not be read, the Maulānā included both *The Bride's Mirror* and *The Daughters of the Bier*, along with two later tales by Naẓīr Aḥmad. Perhaps realizing how odd this would seem to his readers, he added a note of explanation: 'These four books are of the sort that include some points encouraging discernment and decorum but elsewhere have sections that weaken faith.'[12]

His somewhat paradoxical stance is noted by Metcalf: *The Bride's*

---

[10]Minault, *Secluded Scholars*, p. 129.
[11]Naim, 'Prize-Winning *Adab*', p. 300–01.
[12]Metcalf, *Perfecting Women*, pp. 377–80.

Mirror is not only 'the most popularly beloved of the books Thanawi condemns,' but also 'a story that seems in many ways a fictional account of the girl the *Bihishti Zewar* was meant to produce.' Metcalf emphasizes Asghari's exemplary combination of moral qualities and practical abilities:

> It is the story of two sisters, the elder a mean-tempered, uneducated failure and the younger, Asghari, a literate, competent, and pious source of blessing to everyone she encounters. Asghari brings order to household accounts and to people's lives—and is able to correspond with her wise father, who is posted away from home. Patient and sober, she controls her self and her environment.[13]

Why then disapprove of her? C.M. Naim speculates on some possible reasons for the Maulānā's dislike of the tales: Naẓīr Aḥmad's equating of Islam with other religions, his 'praise of the Christian English, at the cost of Muslim Indians,' his mockery of certain types of Muslim religious figures, and 'his portrayal of highly capable and dynamic women, who tower over the men around them.'[14]

A mirror for brides: the Persian 'mirror for princes' genre provides a conceptual starting point. Such a book describes and illustrates good and bad possibilities, providing many moral maxims along the way, so that the prince can see himself as reflecting the virtues and not the vices possible to his office.[15] Naẓīr Aḥmad's bride is to see herself mirrored in Asghari. Just to make sure she takes the point, the author introduces his tale with a long exhortation addressed to the girls who will be reading his book.

He points out to them that women are 'preserved from the toil of earning a livelihood, or making money,' but that 'it is the women who do the entire work of housekeeping.' Thus 'the world is like a cart which cannot move without two wheels—man on one side, and woman on the other' [7]. Women have faculties like those of men, and can become

[13]Metcalf, *Perfecting Women*, p. 326,
[14]Naim, 'Prize-Winning *Adab*', p 308.
[15]For a look at this genre see Levy, *A Mirror for Princes*.

famous like men. It may be true that 'too much learning is unnecessary for a woman,' but still—'how many women are there who acquire even so much as is absolutely necessary?' [8] Girls must learn to write, because they will need to write letters and keep accounts; they should also learn needlework, cooking, and general housekeeping [9–13].

Looking at 'the common practice of the whole country,' we see '*no* value set upon women' (italics Ward's). Yet, 'oh women of India'—and the Urdu has only 'oh women'—you should realize that the blame lies with you: 'It is your fault that you are so fallen in the estimation of the world.' If you acquire more capacity, it will be recognized. Yet living in purdah, how can you acquire it? For this you desperately need literacy. 'For you there is little hope of escape from your seclusion.' For better or worse, the practice is solidly entrenched: 'Public opinion and the custom of the country have made a retired life behind the purdah obligatory and incumbent upon women, and in these days the observance of this institution is more rigid than ever' [15]. Literate, knowledgeable women can educate their children at home, care for them properly, and manage large households more successfully. Everything points to the need for girls to read, to learn! He concludes his long introduction enticingly: 'And now I am going to tell you an amusing story, which will show you what kind of troubles are brought about by a bad education'—literally, by *behunarī*, 'lack of skill' [17].[16]

This sentence seems to promise us chiefly Akbari's story. In fact, Naẕīr Aḥmad divides his tale into two sections. The initial part, Akbari's story, is marked only by the traditional romance-like opening title *Āghāz-e qiṣṣah* (The Beginning of the Story), and indeed the author claims in his introduction to have composed Akbari's story first. But Akbari's story constitutes less than a fifth of the whole narrative. The second section, over four-fifths of the whole, is called *Asġharī Khānam kā bayān* (An Account of the Lady Asghari); this is the part that the author claims he added later at the insistence of his daughters [2]. In his translation G.E. Ward breaks up the text into thirty-one short chapters, of which the first six tell Akbari's story.

Akbari, newly married, behaves in every unsuitable way: consorting with girls of low family, quarrelling with her husband and in-laws,

[16]Naẕīr Aḥmad, *Mirāt*, pp. 24–27.

storming off to her mother's house, refusing to do domestic chores. She sews so sloppily that her aunt not only pinches her, but even runs a needle into her hand by way of punishment. She goes out without her husband's permission, tells her mother false stories of ill-treatment, and spitefully demands an establishment of her own, independent of the joint family home in which she and her husband have been living.

When she does get her own separate household, she is quite unable to run it. She cannot cook, so she feeds herself and her undesirable girlfriends on expensive take-out food from the bazaar. Her girlfriends steal from her, a female con artist and her allies fleece her and run off with her jewels, her unaired clothes are gnawed by ants and rats, and so on.

Why is Akbari such a disaster? We aren't left in any doubt at all. Akbari is awful, her own mother acknowledges, because she was 'her grandmother's spoilt pet,' and her childish disobedience and destructive fits of temper went unchecked [38]. The author endorses this verdict: 'Girls who are perpetually being coddled and indulged when they are little, and who are taught nothing that is useful or practical, invariably reap trouble and sorrow throughout their lives, just like Akbari' [53]. (The story is told by a reliable first-person narrator, but his voice is impossible to distinguish from that of the author.)

✥

Naẓīr Aḥmad helpfully makes the comparison between the sisters' lives as explicit as possible. Although Akbari was sixteen when she was married, he tells us, Asghari was married at the tender age of thirteen— to the less capable, less knowledgeable younger brother of Akbari's husband. Moreover, Asghari had a child in the second year of her married life (though we are later given to understand that this child died soon after birth); and her husband's career obliged her to spend much time away from home. In short, he points out, her situation was worse than Akbari's in every way except one: in childhood she had received 'good training' [58].

For although her mother is 'a very hot-tempered woman', Asghari herself is 'intelligent, sensible, and kindly dispositioned'. She is a paragon: everyone loves her, and her father has entrusted to her the whole management of the household finances [20–21]; she has been running the entire domestic establishment since she was eight years old [61].

Her father, Dūrandesh ('Far-seeing') Khān, sends to her as a wedding present a very long and particularly patriarchal letter of advice about how to behave in her marital home: 'the creation of woman was merely to insure the happiness of man, and it is woman's function to keep man happy' [62]. Asghari makes it her practice 'to read it and meditate upon its contents regularly every day' [66]. In fact, it appears that Asghari has been educated chiefly by her father [126].

Although she finds her life as a new daughter-in-law difficult, Asghari behaves commendably. She cultivates her young sister-in-law, Mahmūdah, and gradually becomes a valued member of the household. But she still runs into trouble. 'Since Asghari was incapable of quarreling, her very accomplishments became the cause of ill will' [68]. She falls foul of Māmā 'Azmat, a venerable female servant who has been presiding over the household for decades, controlling all purchases, all loans and debts, all transactions involving the women's jewels—and, in the process, cheating and stealing to her heart's content. 'In short, Māmā 'Azmat ruled the house, as if she had been a man' [68]. When Asghari catches her out, Māmā 'Azmat conspires to get Asghari into trouble with her in-laws. To make herself indispensable, she exploits the illiteracy and credulousness of Asghari's mother-in-law to persuade her that a harmless sign on the wall is a notice of a lawsuit over the family's chronic indebtedness.

But Asghari has written to her brother, asking him to arrange for her father-in-law to return briefly to Delhi from his post in Lahore. In the meantime, she works quietly to reduce the family's expenses. When her father-in-law arrives, he and she together ensure that Māmā 'Azmat's fraud is exposed and the debts are paid. Asghari's father-in-law addresses her with real respect: he calls her 'brother' [95] and 'son' [108] (the latter shortened by Ward to 'sonnie'), and entrusts her with the management of the household.

The second half of the story (Chapters XVII-XXXI) is an account of how cleverly Asghari manages to restore and increase the family's wealth, while also greatly improving their social connections. She organizes all domestic affairs 'as if the house were a machine, with all its works in good order' [112], and persuades her husband to stop gambling and start working seriously to learn Arabic and accounting.

Her reputation is such that Ḥusnārā, a spoiled young girl from a distantly related aristocratic family of the neighborhood, is sent to her for training. Before long Asghari is running a small girls' school in her home: she teaches reading, writing, and fancy needlework (which is sold to pay the expenses of the school). We learn a lot about her teaching methods (including a recipe for *zardah*), and about the evils of other schools (they are boring, cruel, and exploitative). Asghari's girls dress dolls (thus learning about fabrics, clothes, and festivals), and also have 'doll feasts' that they themselves cook and eat, and for which they keep careful accounts of the costs. In the girls' lessons, Queen Victoria and the Begams of Bhopal serve as inspirations; so do English women who send their children away for schooling, for their love is 'tempered with reason' and is not 'a mad fondness like that of mothers here' who spoil their children and let them run wild [143].

Through Asghari's shrewd advice, discreet politicking, and energetic prodding (she 'put the yoke on' him 'by force' [151]), her husband gets a well-paid appointment in service with the English in Sialkot. At first all is well, but then he falls into bad company and bad habits, and Asghari decides to travel to Sialkot by train, uninvited, to join him. Before her departure, she brings Akbari and her husband (who, like his father, calls Asghari 'brother' [156]) back to the joint family home. She reforms her husband, then returns to Delhi a year and a half later and arranges for her father-in-law to retire and for his older son, Akbari's husband, to take his place.

Her final coup is to take advantage of the love and gratitude felt for her by her now well-trained pupil Husnara and other female allies in that family, in order to get her young sister-in-law Mahmudah married to Husnara's younger brother. She points out, 'Wealth, good qualities, good looks, these are the three main things,' and of them all Mahmudah lacks only wealth [164]; but in accomplishments she is in fact superior to the proposed bridegroom [169]. After much diplomacy and not-so-subtle emotional blackmail, Asghari has her way. She proclaims the virtues of simple marriages; but then, through a number of clever contrivances, she produces far more of a dowry than anyone had expected, so that the marriage takes place in the handsomest style. Because Mahmudah remains devoted to her and constantly seeks her counsel, Asghari now has a chance to manage huge estates, which she does to perfection.

In a brief conclusion we learn that Asghari has left monuments in the world: 'The things which she achieved under these conditions— for all that she was a woman—will no doubt remain in the world as memorials of her to the last day; but unfortunately I have not the leisure to set them down in writing' [187]. We have already had a list, in fact, of a mansion, a mosque, a *sarai*, and various charitable trusts left by her in Delhi [58–59]. She has trials to bear as well: although she has a number of children, most die very young. The death of one much-loved daughter is especially painful to her; however, she endures the blow with dignity and proper religious fortitude. She is consoled by another extremely long and didactic letter from her father that takes up the whole last chapter of the tale. One of her sons lives to adulthood, and is then married to Mahmudah's only daughter.

Naẓīr Ahmad's introduction to the *The Bride's Mirror* is so full of complex feelings for women that it almost shoots out sparks. The reader can easily tell that this writer has spent time with women and girls, and that he genuinely likes them and enjoys their company. He cares enough about them to respect them; he values their potential and wants them to achieve fine things.

Thus he is led into a torrent of reproach. Wanting women to be admirable and admired, he is distressed by the shortcomings he sees in them: ignorance, credulousness, passivity, laziness, emotionalism, superficiality. He illustrates and denounces these faults, trying to hector his young female readers into overcoming such embarrassing, humiliating, even shameful traits.

Yet he also knows that the deck is stacked against women. They cannot (and perhaps should not?) dream of escaping from purdah. Shut up in their houses, denied access to higher education, unable to learn from mingling with the larger world outside, how can they be expected, against all odds, to develop the valuable practical qualities and abilities so much more easily attained by the men of their families?

But at the same time, such qualities and abilities are all the more necessary for women, since they get so little respect at home. If they show extraordinary abilities, they might have a chance to receive a modicum of admiration and attention from the male members of their family. Certainly they have no *other* chance, and Naẕīr Aḥmad tries to goad them into facing this fact. They must think only of life within their family, and within the family they must think of earning the respect of their male relatives, while being careful to maintain their (religiously prescribed) subordinate role in the domestic hierarchy.

Thus every young girl should strive to learn, to become educated, to acquire skills and abilities that will make her shine in the eyes of her family. She should remember that men and women complement each other, they are as mutually indispensable as the two wheels of a cart. Men and women should each strive to shine and excel in their own sphere: women in running the large, complex households of the time, men in earning and managing the money that sustains them. Women must maintain the family's proper order and decorum—which includes their own subordinate and purdah-bound status; men must demonstrate their ability to shelter, support, and protect the women of their family. The cooperative work of both sexes is necessary to maintain the family's status in the world outside.

Naẕīr Aḥmad's tale of two sisters is meant to illustrate how this process can work. The elder sister, Akbari, is a simple textbook example of how to do everything wrong. But Asghari is a far more complicated case. Though she is clearly meant to be a perfect paradigm of feminine behavior, her situation is in fact a limit case, even a liminal case. The story of her life pushes Naẕīr Aḥmad's view far enough to reveal (to the reader if not the author) the paradoxical vision on which it rests.

For Asghari calls into question the neat role division Naẕīr Aḥmad has laid down between men and women; she is almost an honorary man. She is like Athena, born from the forehead of Zeus and thus always favoring the man. Raised by her father, she constantly consults him by letter; she accepts and even reveres his staggeringly male-supremacist dicta. After her marriage, it is not her husband but her father-in-law with whom she consults, and whose unbounded admiration and support she obtains. She is not only an honorary man, but an honorary patriarch: her ties are with older and more powerful men rather than with her own generation. Although she discreetly manages her father-in-law's and older brother-in-law's careers while remaining in the background, she quite openly advises, hectors, and even dominates her hapless husband. When he seems to be going astray,

she travels alone, uninvited and unannounced, to a distant city, where
she immediately takes charge of him, drives away his evil companions,
and reshapes his life to her own virtuous specifications.

She also exercises power through her role as teacher of aristocratic
young girls in the neighborhood, shamelessly twisting the arms of her
two favored pupils in order to marry her young sister-in-law into their
family. At the end of the novel we learn almost as an afterthought that
all her own children died in early childhood. It is hard to imagine her
as a mother. Her legacy is not maternal but material and abstract: she
becomes famous for her buildings and charitable trusts.

How can such unabashed, carefully plotted, meticulously described
manipulation of her whole marital family's fortunes be fitted into her
official ethic of unquestioning subordination to her male elders? It cannot, of course—as the reader will easily notice, but as Naẓīr Aḥmad
apparently did not. Nor did Asghari's marital family notice: all her relatives admired and valued her for her energy, organization, diplomatic
skills, and managerial prowess. What her story really demonstrates is
that in practice, smart, shrewd people (including women) can manipu-
late less capable people (including men) to great advantage. What Asghari's
story shows is that nothing succeeds like success.

❀

In his 'Translator's Note', G.E. Ward praises *The Bride's Mirror* for filling
a gap: 'since so little is known in England about the social and domestic
life of our Indian fellow-subjects, an authentic picture of one phase of
it by a distinguished Muhammadan gentleman may perhaps be not
devoid of interest.' And indeed the story is thoroughly evocative of its
place and time, and fascinatingly full of cultural information. The
lives of the women in a middle-class joint family, their relationships
with the men of the family, their management of a traditional household,
their treatment of servants, their arrangements for marriage, and so on
are narrated with a vividness and colloquial detail that carry immediate
conviction.

David Lelyveld in fact uses the story as an exemplary illustration of
what he calls the 'kacahrī milieu', and points out the characters' betwixt-
and-between financial (and social) position: the family lives comfortably
on an income equal to 'about two percent' of that of the lowest-grade

British civil servant—though such an income was, at the same time, 'twenty or even forty times the wage of a laborer'. In this and other respects, Naẓīr Aḥmad's account 'recapitulates the early careers of Indians in government during the first three-quarters of the nineteenth century'.[17]

Akbari and Asghari have married, we learn, into a good old family that has come down in the world [122–23]. The two sisters' attitudes toward social class, like all their other attitudes, are exactly opposite. The very first quarrel we overhear between Akbari and her husband concerns her habit of associating with the daughters of 'low-bred and vulgar people'. When reproached for this behavior, Akbari is defiant.

The silly wife replied, 'Affection and friendship depend upon the union of hearts. There was a bangle-seller named Basu living next door to my mother's house, whose daughter Banno was my bosom friend. I used to play with her when I was little. Yes, Banno and I made a marriage between our two dolls. Banno, poor thing! was very badly off. I used to steal quantities of things from my mother and give them to her. I would never give up my meetings with Banno, however much my mother forbade them.'

To which her husband replies succinctly, 'A precious idiot you were then!' At this point, 'the foolish woman' reacts with a show of hysteria [18–19]. Unfortunately, she really *is* a foolish, lazy, selfish woman, so that this (to us) attractive display of democratic feeling is developed in the narrative as part of her general gullibility and vulgarity.

By contrast, the newly married Asghari dexterously gets rid of the young girls of the neighborhood, 'especially those of the lower classes', by not offering them sweets when they visit [67]. And when she opens her school, she is ruthless in her social discrimination. 'Asghari picked out those who were born of good parents [sharīf-zādiyāñ], and found some pretext for putting off the others' [125]. But on the other hand, her school offers what amounts to scholarships. Money is earned by the sale of her pupils' embroidery: 'Out of this fund clothes were made and books were purchased for those girls who were poor' [126]. Not money but social class is the real issue. When Asghari plans Mahmudah's marriage, she makes her goal clear: 'It is my wish that she should marry

[17]Lelyveld, *Aligarh's First Generation*, pp. 56, 58.

into a family of very high rank' [145]. There is no sign in the narrative that such social snobbery is anything other than a source of credit to her and her family.

Yet Asghari's values are nothing if not flexible and hard-headedly realistic. She knows how to get the best out of different kinds of employers: local rulers do not pay salaries on time [146], but they do help out with marriage expenses [184]. On the whole, she prefers the English, who look like winners: 'Since the English rule was established', she tells her husband, 'all the native chiefs are in much the same state of decay' [146]. She urges her husband Muhammad Kāmil to start with a humble apprenticeship at the courts, then accept a small post in the system, while looking out for a better one. She tells him it's God's will alone that can get him a position—but also insists that he make his best efforts. She tells him he must rely on himself rather than on others—but then she arranges for powerful family connections to be used on his behalf [146–53].

In short, Asghari covers all the bases, and procures for her docile, naive husband a fine career, and for her whole marital family a rapid rise in the social hierarchy. She is careful not to be gullible, and the result is that she makes no close friends outside her own extended family. She preserves all the outward forms of deference to men and to her elders and to public opinion, but in fact keeps her own counsel and arranges everything as she thinks best. She will never admit to the degree of power that she constantly exercises, for she agrees with Nazīr Ahmad that patriarchal values must be maintained. Men should support the family ('If families are to be reared upon women's earnings, why should there be men?' [155]), and her school, however lucrative, is of no importance compared to her marriage.

All Asghari's central qualities of character emerge clearly in one crucial passage, in which she decides to go to Sialkot, unannounced, to rescue her husband from his evil ways—indebtedness, nautch girls, bad company, bribe-taking—before it is too late. Although she has already made up her mind to go, she discusses the decision with her cousin Tamāshā Khānam [154–55]. Here is my own very literal translation of the heart of that scene.

Tamasha Khanman said, 'To go without being sent for—well, it's not proper.'

Asghari said, 'You're thinking of proper and improper, and I tell you that if I don't go, my home will be ruined for my whole life!'

Tamasha Khanam replied, '*Ai* sister! Why do you lower yourself like this? What do you care about him? May God keep your school safe— you can provide bread for ten people.'

Asghari said, 'A fine idea! What do you understand about it? I've set up this school in order to amuse myself; I never sought to make money from it ... Just think—as if women's earnings are any kind of earnings! If we would habitually run the house on women's earnings, then why would men exist? If my own house is well established, then I don't care even if ten such schools are ruined.'

Tamasha Khanam said, 'How can you go in the midst of the rains? Let the winter come, then in the clear weather you can see about it.'

Asghari said, '*Ai hai*, delay is a disaster! What can now be done by persuasion, can't be done later even by big quarrels.'

Tamasha Khanam said, '*Ai hai*! Doesn't it grieve your heart to leave home?'

Asghari said, 'Why wouldn't it grieve me—am I not human?[18] But is it better to grieve for a little while, or suffer for a lifetime?'

Here is Asghari at her best: energetic, capable, paradoxical, and (most unusually) under intense emotional pressure.

This passage is also offered as a comparison piece, so that the reader can see what Ward has made of it. He himself is very modest and matter-of-fact about his efforts: he describes his translation as 'merely supplementary' to other teaching materials, so that it 'makes no claim to literary merit' (Translator's Note). Ward's style is somewhat more formal and abstract than the Urdu, less colorful, vigorous, and colloquial. But on the whole, he is reasonably faithful to the text, as befits a scholar and language teacher. Only once in a while can one seriously quarrel with him, as in his tendentious rendering of *ādmī* as 'woman' (see footnote 18).

[18]Although the Urdu is *kyā maiñ ādmī nahīñ hūñ?*, the translator renders it 'Am I not a woman?' [155]. In his glossary he defines *ādmī* as 'a descendant of Adam, a man, a woman, a person'; apparently he thinks Asghari is showing distinctively feminine sentiments here.

All this being said, is *The Bride's Mirror* to be considered a novel, or does it remain simply a lively, well-written didactic tale? The author himself does not use the word novel, but does make strong claims to originality: his goal, unusual for the time, is that 'the speech would be idiomatic and the thoughts pure, and no artificiality or embellishment would find entry'. In their prefaces, his British patrons support this claim. Matthew Kempson, the Director of Public Instruction, maintains that the work is unique of its kind: its Urdu is as good as that of Ghalib's letters and the famous romance *Bostān-e Khiyāl*, and it is so free of 'romantic themes' and high-flown literary and rhetorical devices that everyone ought to copy it. The Lieutenant Governor agrees: 'no other book in Urdu is its equal.'[19]

Some critics have considered it a novel, and even a very fine one. The enthusiastic Shaistah Akhtar Banu Suhrawardy, writing in 1945, declares *The Bride's Mirror* to be 'the first real novel in Urdu, and still the best'. Making her case at length, she emphasizes its 'superb and masterly characterisation,' so that the characters appear real, living, and timelessly appealing. She finds that Nazīr Ahmad's work marks a great advance beyond the traditional Urdu romances (*dāstān*) with their worlds full of heroes meeting implausible, supernatural adventures.[20]

Other critics consider it a novel, but a flawed one. The well-known historian of Urdu literature Muhammad Sadiq finds such flaws unsurprising, since the author is seeking 'to supply textbooks for juvenile readers'. Since Nazīr Ahmad is a moralist, 'the course of his stories is entirely directed by didactic considerations': he 'invents a story in strict accordance with a thesis, and then fits it out with ready-made characters'. Even so, he has 'a keen sense of comedy' and a 'sufficiently wide' range of humor to keep his stereotyped characters alive and overcome the lack of dialogue and 'unusually slow tempo' of his 'thin and unequal' plots.[21]

To Iftikhār Ahmad Siddīqī, an especially close student of Nazīr Ahmad's work, *The Bride's Mirror* is a novel badly marred by the way 'the story's plot has been bifurcated' by didactic pressures: the stories of

---

[19]Nazīr Ahmad, *Mirāt ul-'Arūs*, pp. 3–5, 7.
[20]Suhrawardy, *The Development of the Urdu Novel*, pp. 25–26, 40–41, 43.
[21]Sadiq, *A History of Urdu Literature*, pp. 410–14.

Akbari and Asghari have 'no relationship except that they are the stories of two sisters'. The novel offers few of the traditional narrative pleasures, and especially lacks 'conflict' and 'suspense'. In fact, 'the worst flaw of Asghari's character is that she is flawless, like *dāstān* characters.' For 'the novelist has bestowed on Asghari such exemplary excellence that all the rest of the characters are humbled [*dab kar rah ga'e*] before her.'[22] (This observation agrees with Naim's conjecture about why Maulānā Ashraf 'Alī Thānavī condemned the book.)

Ralph Russell, by contrast, defends Naẓīr Aḥmad by denying that he is a novelist. It is unfair to judge him as a novelist, since 'he himself to the end of his days never made any claim to be one.' He wrote to instruct, and 'chose a fictional form because in that way he could make his instruction more palatable'. Although not a novelist, he 'was one of the founders of the modern Urdu novel, and this is his main importance in the history of Urdu literature.' We should remember that his many contributions transcended the merely literary: he was 'an outstandingly able translator, a sound practical educationist, the greatest orator the Aligarh movement produced, and a powerful and original religious thinker'.[23]

Elsewhere, however, Russell speaks of the 'novels and other writings' of Naẓīr Aḥmad, an author 'whose vivid, magnificent Urdu prose far surpasses that of any other nineteenth-century writer and affords me some of my favourite reading'.[24] Perhaps then Russell would consider him a kind of proto-novelist.

To me, *The Bride's Mirror* is ultimately a fascinating hybrid, a conceptual football ideally suited to be kicked around by theorists of the novel. It has some *dāstān*-like qualities; inserted stories [35–36, 46–47]; an abrupt, episodic structure; an omnipotent and authoritarian narrator; stylized characters with distinctive, memorable traits that rarely change; a great fondness for long formal letters; and a tendency to spin off casual promises of more stories yet to come [125, 144, 192].

Yet clearly its original impulse was British-influenced, reformist, and didactic. The fact that Naẓīr Aḥmad had a satiric eye and a gift for lively

[22]Ṣiddīqī, *Maulvī Naẓīr Aḥmad*, pp. 336–37, 342–43.
[23]Russell, *The Pursuit of Urdu Literature*, pp. 92, 112.
[24]Russell, *Hidden in the Lute*, p. 3.

dialogue simply meant that the pill had more sugar on it than a lesser writer could have provided. As we have seen, the author proclaimed his hostility to artifice and embellishment—a slap at traditional Persianized Urdu poetry and prose—and his allegiance to colloquial language and 'pure thoughts'. (Whether he was writing for his daughters or for Matthew Kempson, the same stylistic choices proved equally pleasing to both.) *The Bride's Mirror* takes place in a historically accurate, minutely detailed social space, and all the events in it are brought about by normal, rationally explicable (and explicated) causes. The powers of its heroes and villains are on a human scale. In all these ways it is more like a 'novel' than a romance (*dāstān*).

And yet, the term 'novel' itself is so (in)famously flexible. Strange, hybrid, soi-disant 'novels' are no modern monopoly. An English translation of the most famous Urdu romance was itself published in 1892 as *An Oriental Novel: Dastan-e Amir Hamza*. In his preface, the translator describes the work as 'a beautiful Oriental novel' which 'is very much to the taste of native readers'. However, he does not find it free of flaws. 'As is the case with native novelists,' the story is 'ornamented by numerous exaggerations and colorings', and he has sought to minimize such 'superfluities'.[25] But of course, one reader's—or one culture's, or one generation's—grotesque hyperbole is another's marvelous inventiveness. The debate about 'novelness' is not one that can ever be finally resolved.

In any case, what Naẕīr Aḥmad promises us in his tale of Akbari and Asghari is not a novel but a *laṭīf qiṣṣah*,[26] a refined, graceful, subtle, agreeable story. For well over a century readers have been discovering with pleasure how amply he fulfills this promise.

Frances W. Pritchett
Columbia University

---

[25]Hosain, *An Oriental Novel*, pp. 3–4. See also Pritchett, *The Romance Tradition in Urdu*.

[26]Naẕīr Aḥmad, *Mirat ul-'Arūs*, p. 27.

BIBLIOGRAPHY

Gupta, Narayani. *Delhi Between Two Empires 1803–1931: Society, Government and Urban Growth*. Delhi: Oxford University Press, 1981.

Hosain, Sheik Sajjad, trans. *An Oriental Novel: Dastan-e Amir Hamza*. Patna: Khuda Bakhsh Oriental Public Library, [1892] 1922.

Kalsi, A.S. 'The Influence of Nazir Ahmad's *Mirāt al-'Arūs* (1869) on the Development of Hindi Fiction.' *Annual of Urdu Studies* 7 (1990): 31–44.

Kempson, Matthew, trans. *The Repentance of Nussooh*. London: W.H. Allen & Co., 1884.

Lelyveld, David. *Aligarh's First Generation: Muslim Solidarity in British India*. Princeton: Princeton University Press, 1978.

Levy, Reuben, trans. *A Mirror for Princes: The Qabus Nama*. New York: E.P. Dutton, 1951.

Metcalf, Barbara. *Perfecting Women: Maulana Ashraf Ali Thanawi's Bihishti Zewar*. Berkeley: University of California Press, 1990.

Minault, Gail. *Secluded Scholars: Women's Education and Muslim Social Reform in Colonial India*. Delhi: Oxford University Press, 1998.

Naim, C.M. 'Prize-Winning *Adab*: A Study of Five Urdu Books Written in Response to the Allahabad Government Gazette Notification.' In *Moral Conduct and Authority: The Place of Adab in South Asian Islam*. Barbara Daly Metcalf, ed. Berkeley: University of California Press, 1984, pp. 290–314.

Naẓīr Aḥmad. *Mirāt ul-'Arūs*. Lucknow: Tej Kumār Book Depot, [1869] 1978. [Urdu.]

Pritchett, Frances W. *The Romance Tradition in Urdu: Adventures from the Dāstān-e Amīr Ḥamzah*. New York: Columbia University Press, 1991.

Russell, Ralph. *The Pursuit of Urdu Literature: A Select History*. London: Zed Books Ltd., 1992.

————. *Hidden in the Lute: An Anthology of Two Centuries of Urdu Literature.* New Delhi: Viking, 1995.

Sadiq, Muhammad. *A History of Urdu Literature.* Delhi: Oxford University Press, 1984.

Ṣiddīqī, Iftiḳhār Aḥmad. *Maulvī Naẓīr Aḥmad Dihlavī: aḥvāl oāśār.* Lahore: Majlis Taraqqī-e Adab, 1971. [Urdu.]

Suhrawardy, Shaista Akhtar Banu. *A Critical Survey of the Development of the Urdu Novel and Short Story.* London: Longmans, Green and Co., 1945.

Ward, G.E., trans. *The Bride's Mirror: A Tale of Domestic Life in Delhi Forty Years Ago.* London: Henry Frowde, 1903.

————. *The Bride's Mirror, or Mir-atu l-arūs of Maulavi naẓir-Aḥmad.* Edited (by Permission of the Author) in the Roman Character, With a Vocabulary and Notes. London: Henry Frowde, 1899.